Living With PTSD

PTSD Recovery

Tim L. Gardner

Table of Contents

Introduction

"There is no timestamp on trauma. There isn't a formula that you can insert yourself into to get from horror to healed. Be patient. Take up space. Let your journey be the balm."

-    by Dawn Serra

Post Traumatic Stress Disorder or PTSD is a condition that affects individuals from various parts of life. Many people tend to deal with this problem after they have dealt with traumatic events like combat, domestic violence, natural disasters, accidents, and loss of a loved one. Women are also more prone to this condition because they are more exposed to sexual traumas like rape and other similar problems.

Still, this does not imply that everyone can't experience trauma in their life. Consider the following PTSD statistics:

- 70% of adults' deal with no less than one traumatic event during their lives

- 20% of the individuals who suffer deal with a traumatic event will get PTSD

- One in 13 individuals will get PTSD at some aspect in their life

- About Eight million individuals have PTSD in a year

With the stats above, you can understand how serious this condition is. Even if you don't have PTSD, there is a huge chance that someone you know might have the condition. This condition can affect the quality of a person's life with symptoms like flashbacks, nightmares, sadness, guilt, shame, anxiety, anger, and depression.

All of these can make it impossible to live a healthy life and can affect the person's family, relationships, and work-life. This means if you or someone you know is experiencing PTSD, it is incredibly crucial that you begin to look for a solution now.

Many people have tried to handle PTSD by themselves and only found themselves right back where they started. This is to be expected because PTSD is a condition that you need to attack on all fronts, starting at the mind and moving on to the body and your habits.

With the right information from an experienced source telling you what to do, you can surely free yourself. Many people have addressed their PTSD and moved on to the future they envisioned.

The good news is that this is the right book to provide all the knowledge you require to free yourself from this condition and start your journey of recovery. In this book, you will learn what PTSD is along with some of the following:

- The symptoms and causes of PTSD

- Treatment options available

- How Journaling can help

- Communicating with your friends and family about your condition

- Self-care strategies

- Saving your relationships etc.

These and many more are some of the things you stand to gain from reading this book. PTSD is a condition that can break down all areas of your life until you are alone and suffering from depression. And if you fail to begin treatment as soon as possible, you may be stuck with the condition for the remainder of your life.

In order to ensure this does not happen, you need to begin treatment today using all of the information that has been put together in this book. Time waits for no one, and the longer you wait, the worse your PTSD symptoms might become. Make a move now! Do not wait it out in the hopes that the symptoms might vanish on their own because they hardly ever do.

I have seen firsthand the damage PTSD is capable of. My sister dealt with this problem for a long time after an abusive relationship. Her problem worsened after I finished my business degree and opened up my coffee shop.

Soon, she was isolating herself and trying to push everyone out, including me. Some days, it took something very minor to trigger her, and I desperately searched for a way to help her recover. When she had an outburst of anger one evening, it all fell in place.

I knew at that point that it was time for me to take action, and I took up a psychology degree online on the side. With my degree and interaction with my sister, I was able to help her out of her predicament. It took almost two years to get her life back on track, but it was a fulfilling and learning experience for us as a family.

It took me years to earn my degree, but seeing what my sister went through, I wanted to better understand how human behavior works so I can ensure no one else experiences the same thing my sister did. With all of the information and experience I have attained over the years, I have helped many people through their condition and wish to help more people.

You and your loved one can be happy. There is indeed treatment for people living with PTSD, as there is an increase in the availability of PTSD treatment. According to PTSD treatment statistics, the results for treatment have been positive. A study also revealed that as many as 46% of individuals dealing with PTSD improved in the initial six weeks of starting psychotherapy. Researchers have also revealed that as much as 62% of individuals who are getting medication for the condition are showing improvement.

PTSD is a serious issue and one that should not be undermined. Even if you don't have it, you can keep yourself informed to help someone you know get past this dark part of their lives.

Chapter 1:

Understanding Your State

As with any other condition a person can experience, the first thing you will have to do in order to find a cure is to understand PTSD. In this chapter, we will be looking into PTSD, including its symptoms, causes, and all other vital information you will require to understand the condition.

What is PTSD?

Post-traumatic stress disorder or PTSD is a severe mental disorder that some individuals develop after a dangerous, shocking, or scary occurrence. These kinds of occurrences are known as traumas.

Once a person has experienced trauma, it is common to deal with anxiety, misery, and even fear. You may have memories that upset you or have problems sleeping. For typical individuals, these feelings fade over time, and things get better.

However, these feelings and thoughts remain in someone dealing with PTSD. They can last for months and even years, and they can become even more critical as time goes on.

PTSD can affect all aspects of your life, including your personal life and your life at work. It can also have an impact on your emotional and physical health. Still, with the right form of treatment, there is a chance for you to live the kind of life you desire.

How Does PTSD Happen?

When you experience a traumatic event, your body has a natural "flight or fight" response. When this happens, it lets out stress hormones like norepinephrine and adrenaline to give you an energy surge. Then your heart begins to beat at a faster pace, and your brain pauses some of its normal tasks like storing short-term memories.

When this is working as it should, it is not a bad thing as it is how your body protects you from danger. But when you are dealing with PTSD, it can be a problem as it could cause your brain to stay stranded in danger mode. So even when there is no imminent danger, your brain remains on high alert, and your body keeps on sending out stress signals. This can result in PTSD symptoms.

PTSD tends to change your brain with time as it makes the area that controls your memory smaller. This area is known as the hippocampus. The possible alteration of the hippocampus by PTSD is one of the major reasons many professionals recommend that you get treated as soon as possible.

What are The Symptoms of PTSD?

You may experience numerous symptoms when dealing with PTSD. These could range from emotional numbness, feelings of guilt, angry outbursts, and so on. In some cases, you may stay away from things that bring memories of your trauma and start to lose interest in things you once loved.

Symptoms usually begin after three months of experiencing the traumatic event. Nonetheless, they may not become evident until after a few years and can last for as long as a month. If you don't get the right kind of treatment as soon as possible, you can deal with PTSD for many years or even for the rest of your life.

Your feelings may fluctuate over time. You could feel worse today and better tomorrow, depending on the triggers in your environment. For instance, a movie about someone losing a loved one may trigger memories of the loved one you lost a while back.

PTSD can make it more difficult for you to interact with others, solve problems, or even trust other people. It can also bring about issues in your relationships with family, friends, and even coworkers. Studies have also shown that it increases the probability of you dealing with digestive disorders and heart problems.

For an individual to be diagnosed with PTSD, they will have to meet standards put in place by the Diagnostic and Statistical Manual Fifth Edition or DSM-5 of the American Psychological Association or APA.

As stated by these guidelines, the individual must:

Have come in contact with a serious injury, threatened death or death, sexual violence either through seeing it happening or having experienced it themselves. They could also have been exposed to any of these issues during their professional obligations.

Have experienced the following for one month or more:

- Intrusion symptoms: One or more

- Avoidance symptoms: One or more

- Two or more symptoms that have an impact on thinking or mood

- Two or more symptoms of reactivity and arousal that started after being exposed to the trauma

Below are a few examples of each of these symptoms:

Intrusion symptoms: These take place when an individual can't stop reliving a traumatic occurrence through memories, dreams, and flashbacks.

A few examples of these symptoms include:

- Fearful thoughts

- Nightmares

- Flashback and feeling that the event is taking place once more

Avoidance symptoms: Individuals dealing with these symptoms avoid feelings, people, places, or thoughts that they link with the traumatic event.

A few examples of these symptoms include:

- Blatantly refusing to speak about the event

- Staying away from situations that make them remember the event

- Arousal and reactivity symptoms

- Problems sleeping

- Angry outbursts which could be verbal or physical

- Hypersensitivity to probable dangers which may lead to them being startled with ease

- Feeling anxious and tense

Symptoms That Have an Impact on Thinking and Mood

- Feelings of blame and guilt

- Problems focusing or concentrating

- Inability to recollect some parts of the event

- Feeling of detachment from others and mental and emotional numbness

- Losing interest in life

- Mental health issues like anxiety and depression

Also, the symptoms have to result in issues coping with relationships or work. They must also result in distress and shouldn't be due to the use of medication or substance abuse. It should also not be due to other health problems.

Physical Symptoms

In addition to the above, PTSD could also have physical symptoms that are not a part of the DSM-5 criteria. They include:

- Weak immune system which could result in more infections.

- Stomach problems, chest pain, shaking dizziness, sweating, headaches, and shaking.

- Sleep disruptions could lead to tiredness and other issues.

There may also be long term changes to the behavior of the individual. This could lead to broken relationships and other problems at work. Also, the individual may start drinking more alcohol than before or begin to abuse drugs and other substances.

Children and Teens

Children who are six or younger may deal with PTSD symptoms which range from:

- Problems speaking

- Over clinginess to adults

- Lashing out while playing

- Bedwetting after being bathroom trained

When a child gets between the ages of five to 12, they may not have problems remembering aspects of the events, or may not suffer flashbacks. But, they may believe that there was a sign that the trauma was going to occur. In other cases, they may remember the event in a different order.

Sometimes, they may express this trauma through stories, play, and pictures. They may find it difficult to spend time with friends, go to school, and study. They could also be ill-tempered and have nightmares.

Kids around eight years and above may show signs similar to those of adults. They may consider vengeance as an option or deal with guilt for reacting the way they did when the event occurred.

Kids who dealt with sexual abuse may experience:

- Sadness, isolation, feeling of fear and anxiety

- Self- harm

- Alcohol or drug abuse

- Bursts of anger

- Display of unusual sexual behavior

PTSD Screening

A person may be given a screening test to determine if they have PTSD. The test may include numerous sessions broken down into 15 minutes to one hour each. If there is a legal implication attached, the session could be longer.

If symptoms leave after some weeks, the individual may be diagnosed with acute stress disorder. This is because PTSD is usually not brief and also comes with more severe symptoms. What's more, the symptoms may not show up until long after the trauma.

Most people can recover within six months; however, some people continue to deal with the symptoms for numerous years.

Causes of PTSD

A variety of factors may cause PTSD. Some of the most common ones include:

Military Service and Combat

This is one of the most common reasons why people experience PTSD. According to the National Center for PTSD, an estimate of 11 – 20% of veterans who served in Iraq and Afghanistan wars deal with PTSD.

Approximately 30% of those who served in Vietnam have been diagnosed with this condition at one point during their lives. There are many triggers on the battlefield, which could cause trauma ranging from bombings, deaths of squad members, ambushes, and gunfire.

All of these make it understandable that military combat is a major cause of this disorder.

Severe Road Accident

Most accidents are not serious enough to result in a mental disorder. However, a severe accident that involves casualties could be very traumatizing for anyone, particularly if any of those casualties are loved ones. These sorts of accidents have a likelihood of causing flashbacks and probably PTSD.

In some cases, it could be that the accident was unusually large, with many vehicles engulfed in flames. After this, the individual may experience flashbacks when on the road or in similar situations. If they had the accident due to a brake failure, they may have flashbacks or become anxious when they try to use the brake in the future.

Extended Abuse

When a person deals with severe sexual abuse, neglect, or physical abuse, it can leave behind devastating and permanent damage. In most cases, abuse survivors tend to develop mental disorders like depression, PTSD, and even anxiety. However, with the right form of treatment, these sorts of individuals can get their lives back on track.

Personal Assaults

Numerous individuals develop PTSD after experiencing a violent personal assault. This assault could be in the form of a robbery, mugging, rape, or other similar occurrences. If the individual was scared for their safety during the event, it could easily result in PTSD.

Terrorist Attacks

Not everyone may experience this; however, people who are situated in areas prone to terrorist attacks may experience nightmares and flashbacks. Terrorist attacks are extremely stressful and distressing. They can result in PTSD symptoms and nightmares that could last for decades.

The Loss of a Loved One

Someone dies every day in various parts of the world. To you, it may be just another figure, but this death could result in PTSD for those who were close to this person. This is usually the case if the loved one suffered an extremely violent death in the presence of the individual. These forms of deaths could result in flashbacks and nightmares for years to come.

Receiving A Lethal Diagnosis

It can be traumatic to learn that you have only a few years to live. This is usually not the case for many people. But in some cases, it could result in fear and shock, which are enough to trigger nightmares centered around the person thinking of the unknown.

In essence, almost any event that results in helplessness, shock, fear, and horror can result in PTSD.

PTSD Risk Factors

It is not still clear as to why some individuals experience PTSD while others don't. However, there are a few risk factors that may heighten the possibility of dealing with symptoms like:

- Absence of social support after an event.

- History of substance use

- Previous abuse experience.

- Having health problems before experiencing trauma or due to the trauma.

- Having more problems after a traumatic event. For instance, being in an accident and losing a loved one.

In some cases, genetics may have a role to play as well. This may affect the possibility of experiencing depression, anxiety, and PTSD. Other potential causes of PTSD include:

Survival Mechanism

There is a suggestion that people experience PTSD symptoms due to our natural survival mechanisms, which aims to protect you from more traumas. For instance, if you have nightmares that are common with PTSD, it may force you to analyze an event critically, so you prepare yourself if it takes place once more.

Flashbacks may also offer you the same benefit as nightmares. A hypersensitivity to danger may occur so you can react fast if another dangerous event takes place.

However, even though these responses mean well, they are doing more harm than good. This is because you fail to process a traumatic event and move on.

High Levels of Adrenaline

According to studies, individuals who experience PTSD have an unusual level of stress hormones. Ideally, a "fight or flight" response triggers when you're in danger. Before getting into this mode, your body produces stress hormones like adrenaline to help trigger it.

When in this mode, your senses are deadened, and you don't feel as much pain. Individuals suffering from this disorder have been observed to constantly produce high amounts of these hormones needed for "fight or flight" even when there is no danger.

It is believed that this is what triggers the hyperarousal and dead emotions, several individuals with PTSD experience.

Alterations in the Brain

Parts of the brain that have to do with emotional processing are different in people with PTSD during brain scans. In these individuals, the hippocampus, which is the aspect of the brain responsible for emotions and memory, appears smaller in size.

It is believed that the changes to this aspect of the brain may be involved with anxiety, fear, flashbacks, and memory issues. A hippocampus that is not functioning well may prevent one from correctly processing nightmares and flashbacks. As a result, the anxiety they cause does not reduce with time.

Memories can be processed correctly after PTSD is treated, causing nightmares and flashbacks to vanish slowly.

Gender

Studies have shown that women have a higher tendency of experiencing PTSD, while men may experience violence.

How Can the Risk Be Minimized?

Experts are observing factors that may help ensure people do not get PTSD in the first place or recover fully.

Some of these include:

- Getting support from others.

- Developing coping techniques.

- The ability of the person to feel good about their behavior when difficult times set in.

When Should You Head To A Doctor?

If you are involved in a traumatic event, you may experience a few symptoms. Some of these may include anxiety, difficulty concentrating, and crying. However, this may not be PTSD symptoms.

Still, to ensure the symptoms don't blow up and worsen, you may need to seek the help of an expert.

You need to consider treatment if:

- You are considering self-harm.

- You have been experiencing the symptoms for over a month.

- The symptoms are preventing you from experiencing a normal life.

Related Conditions To PTSD

If you do not meet every criterion to be medically diagnosed with this disorder, there are a few related conditions you may possess instead. Some of which include:

Acute Stress Disorder

This is a response to a traumatic occurrence similar to PTSD, and It also shares the same kind of symptoms. However, these symptoms can start to manifest three days to a month after the experience. People with this disorder may feel numb, experience nightmares or flashbacks, and relive the experience.

All of these symptoms are not comfortable and can lead to issues in their everyday lives. Around half of the individuals who experience this condition end up suffering from PTSD.

Around 14-20% of individuals who survive car accidents tend to develop this disorder, while around

25-50% of those who survive rape, assaults, and mass shootings develop the condition.

Cognitive behavior therapy can help prevent this condition from worsening and transforming into full-blown PTSD. Some medications can also help suppress the symptoms like SSRI antidepressants.

Adjustment Disorder

This takes place as a reaction to a stressful life situation. The behavioral or emotional symptom experienced by a person as a reaction to the stressor does not usually align. In most cases, it is more intense and severe than what one would ideally expect from the kind of event.

Symptoms of adjustment disorder could include the following:

- Self-isolation

- Hopelessness and Sadness

- Impulsive behavior

- Physical symptoms like headaches and tremors

These symptoms can affect every area of a person's life ranging from social interaction, work, and school life. Symptoms of this condition become evident within three months of experiencing a stressful situation. However, it does not last beyond six months after the stressor's effect has worn off.

The stressor could be a combination of various events, or it could be a single event like an accident. Stressors could also be ongoing, like a persistent and painful illness. It is also possible for a stressor to affect a community, family, or a single person. This disorder is usually treated with the help of psychotherapy.

Disinhibited Social Engagement Disorder

This takes place in kids who have suffered from deprivation or social neglect before two years of age. This condition can manifest when children don't have the basic emotional requirements for affection, comfort, and stimulation. It could also occur when caregivers are changed constantly, preventing children from establishing stable bonds and relationships.

This disorder has to do with a kid being extremely familiar with an unknown adult. For instance, a child may willingly tag along with an adult they have never met or don't know without any arguments. This sort of behavior can be problematic for the child later on as it can affect their ability to relate to their age group and adults properly.

A good way to improve this symptom is to move the child to an environment where they get all their basic needs. Still, there are cases where these symptoms may linger on even with the change of environment. Some kids may continue to experience these symptoms until they are adolescents.

In addition to this disorder, there may be delays in the development of the childlike language and cognitive delays. This disorder is considered uncommon because many children that have been neglected usually don't experience this disorder. To get treatment, the family and the child need to seek the help of an experienced therapist to help strengthen their relationship.

Reactive Attachment Disorder

This takes place in children who were socially deprived or abandoned during their initial years of life. This condition can manifest in similar situations to the disinhibited social engagement disorder discussed above.

Children with this condition are not emotionally attached to their adult caregivers. They hardly turn to caregivers when they require protection, support, or comfort. Neither do they respond when they are distressed and comforted by caregivers. They may display inexplicable sadness or fear and show little positive emotions.

The issues become evident before they get to five years of age. In addition to this, the children may experience various developmental delays alongside language and cognitive delays. Similar to the above, treatment will involve the family and child working alongside a therapist to develop a stronger bond.

Other Problems

People dealing with PTSD may also battle other issues, some of which include:

- Mental problems like anxiety, depression, or phobias.

- Destructive behavior like alcohol and drug abuse or self-harming.

- Various physical symptoms include chest pains, dizziness, and stomach aches.

Although there may not be a specific cure in place for PTSD, there are various options for treatment available. With the appropriate kind of support, it is possible for patients to start the process of healing.

Depending on how severe the condition of the patient is, they may be able to combine medication, talk therapy, cognitive behavioral therapy, and other forms of treatment to start recovery.

In the next chapter, we will be taking a look at some of these treatment options, and all you need to know about them.

Chapter 2:

Road to Recovery

PTSD is a disorder that is highly inconveniencing. When you are dealing with this disorder, it may seem like there is no escape in sight. However, the truth is that it can be treated.

Similar to many forms of mental illnesses, there is no cure in existence for PTSD. Still, there are many ways to manage the symptoms and help the individual get back a feeling of normal life.

The best strategy for dealing with this condition is a combination of therapy and medication. By collaborating with a healthcare expert, people dealing with this condition get over their triggers, learn how to cope with the stress, and get over the trauma.

Let's take a look at some of the primary treatment options for this condition, starting with psychotherapy.

Psychotherapy

There are numerous kinds of psychotherapy, also known as talk therapy. You can use any of these to treat adults and kids with this condition.

All forms of PTSD therapy have three major objectives which are:

- To teach you the skills required to handle it.

- Improve the symptoms.

- Reestablish your self-esteem.

The majority of therapies for PTSD can be categorized under cognitive-behavioral therapy (CBT). The goal is to replace those thought patterns that are causing a disruption to a person's life. You may achieve this by talking about your traumatic experience or paying attention to the areas that bring you fear.

Based on your situation, family or group therapy may be an ideal option for you as opposed to individual sessions.

Some of the psychotherapy methods used in treating PTSD are discussed below.

Cognitive Processing Therapy (CPT)

This is a treatment that lasts for 12 weeks, with sessions of 60 -90 minutes weekly. CPT allows you to manage problems by thinking more positively, thereby freeing you from unhealthy behavior patterns.

Trauma-focused CPT utilizes various psychological strategies to help you accept traumatic occurrences.

For instance, your therapist may urge you to challenge memories that cause you trauma by thinking about them in detail. While this is going on, the therapist helps you deal with any agony you feel. The therapist will help you point out any unhelpful thoughts that you suffer from due to the trauma.

For instance, if you are feeling guilty for reacting the way you did during the trauma, the therapist can help ensure you don't feel this way anymore. With time, you may be urged to slowly start engaging in activities that you stayed away from after your experience.

Pros of CPT

- It can be efficient in situations where only medication has not worked.

- The timeframe for completion is short in comparison to many other alternatives.

- It can help you retain your thoughts and change your behavior, which all help you change the way you feel.

Cons

- You will need to cooperate to get results. The therapist won't be able to get rid of your problems without you making an effort.

- It can be time-consuming.

- It may not be ideal for individuals who have more complicated mental health requirements.

Prolonged Exposure Therapy

If you tend to avoid things that remind you of your previous traumatic experience, then prolonged exposure therapy is your best bet. It consists of eight to 15 sessions that usually last around 90 minutes per session.

During the initial phase of the treatment, the therapist will teach you some breathing strategies, which will help in easing your anxiety anytime you think about the event that occurred. Once this is done, you will need to list things you have been avoiding and learn how to deal with them one at a time.

In a later session, you will narrate the traumatic event to your therapist while being recorded. Then, after the session, you will go home and listen to your narration.

Doing this frequently can help ease your symptoms.

Pros

- It offers fast results.

- It teaches you to face your fears.

Cons

- It is not easy to administer.

- It is time-consuming.

- You may need to face your fears, which may not be easy for many individuals.

Eye Movement Desensitization and Reprocessing (EMDR)

EMDR works with the concept that with the help of psychotherapy, you can aid the mind in healing itself. This is similar to how the body heals after a scrape or cut. This basically teaches your brain to process things in a new light and let go of the trauma caused by specific memories, before finally releasing your mind from the old attachments.

EMDR emphasizes getting rid of these mental blocks and letting your brain get past old emotional issues. In this case, you may not need to tell your therapist about the experience causing your trauma.

Instead, it is a combination of motivating sounds and images. The therapist utilizes auditory sounds and movement of the eyes to help you get to the point where you don't experience anguish anytime you relive a memory.

The objective is to be able to think positive thoughts while thinking of your trauma. It requires weekly sessions spanning up to three months.

Pros

- It helps you reveal previous trauma so you can start true healing.

- It provides quick relief.

- It can treat a variety of symptoms.

- You don't have to tell the therapist about your traumatic experience.

- It does not have any side effects.

Cons

Compared to other forms of therapies, EMDR has a short history. For this reason, it is impossible to tell how effective it is.

Stress Inoculation Training (SIT)

This is another form of CBT that you can do in a group or by yourself. Similar to the above method, you won't need to go into detail about the event that occurred. This method emphasizes changing the way you handle stress from the event.

You may have to learn breathing techniques, massage, and other methods to stop negative thoughts by keeping your body and mind relaxed. Ideally, you should have all you need to let go of all the stress from your life after about three months.

Medications

As we discussed earlier, individuals dealing with PTSD may have changed. Individuals dealing with this condition tend to process danger differently.

With the help of medications, you can stop reliving what happened and responding to it. You can stop flashbacks and nightmares too. The right medication can help you see life more positively and function properly once more.

Various kinds of drugs influence the aspects of your brain that have to do with anxiety and fear. Doctors typically begin with medications that affect the neurotransmitters norepinephrine or serotonin (SNRIs and SSRIs).

Some examples of these also include:

- Venlafaxine (Effexor)

- Paroxetine (Paxil)

- Fluoxetine (Prozac)

- Sertraline (Zoloft)

Sertraline and paroxetine are the only medications that have been approved for the treatment of PTSD.

Although there are common diagnoses and treatment methods, everyone's manifestation of PTSD is unique. This means your PTSD won't be the same as someone you know, and you won't respond to medications in the same manner either.

For this reason, your physician may recommend other medications that may not have been shown to be effective solely for PTSD. Some of these may consist of:

- Antidepressants

- Antipsychotics or second-generation antipsychotics (SGAs)

- Monoamine oxidase inhibitors (MAOIs)

- Benzodiazepines

- Beta-blockers

It is fine to utilize off-label medications if your physician recommends them to you.

Medications can aid you in dealing with specific symptoms or other problems that may have developed as a result of your condition. For instance, prazosin may help deal with nightmares.

You may have to use a combination of different medications to tackle your condition properly. However, your ideal combination is dependent on the types of symptoms you are dealing with, the side effects of the medications, and if you also have other associated problems like substance abuse, depression, and anxiety.

It may require some time to get the ideal dosage for some medications. This is because specific medications might require you to go for frequent tests. Testing may be needed to determine if your vital organs are in peak condition and if they will be able to handle the drug. You may also need to do a few tests with your doctor to determine the likely side effects.

Medications may not completely eradicate all of your symptoms, but they are ideal options for making them more manageable so you can function properly.

Other Medications

Your physician may also prescribe other forms of medications like the anti-hypertensive alpha-blocker prazosin to help minimize the symptoms of PTSD. Since everyone does not respond in the same manner, it may require some time to find the ideal medication for you. It will be important to have a medical expert by your side during this process to get you the ideal medications.

However, the downside of medications is that they may cause side-effects. Some of these may include:

- Dizziness

- Agitation

- Drowsiness

- Nausea

- Headaches

- Insomnia

If you observe any of these symptoms, it is best to reach out to your physician for the next step.

Other Alternative Therapies

If actual therapy is not an option for you, then there are many alternative therapies that could also provide you results. A few of these are:

Trauma-Sensitive Yoga

Yoga is something that has been known to offer benefits to people in different age groups. This is also the case for stress relief and those dealing with mental health issues. However, people with PTSD are not left out as this form of yoga can be extremely beneficial.

Trauma-sensitive yoga was initially introduced by David Emerson. According to the research he carried out with Bessel van der Kolk, who is a trauma expert, it was proven that this form of yoga helped to drastically minimize the symptoms of PTSD in participants. As opposed to other forms of yoga, this yoga places emphasis on minimal hands-on adjustment and calmer movements.

Acupuncture

This is a healing practice that originated in China. It has to do with placing thin needles into specific areas of the body to relieve or avert health problems.

The Department of Veterans Affairs has approved this practice as a legitimate alternative medicine treatment for this condition. Numerous studies have shown that this method of treatment is budget-friendly and safe. Many patients who used this treatment method have stated that they felt less anxiety and stress after the procedure.

Ketamine Infusion

The FDA initially approved Ketamine for use as anesthesia. However, it is rising as a good choice for treating conditions that have to do with mental health like PTSD. It is administered through the veins at a low dose that makes it secure for treatment without resulting in any severe side effects.

According to research, one session of ketamine infusion lasting for around 40 minutes can drastically reduce symptoms of PTSD. Only a trained medical expert is allowed to give this type of treatment. There is still ongoing research as to the best way to apply this form of treatment going forward.

MDMA-Assisted Therapy

This is popularly recognized as ecstasy, a recreational drug. However, there is research working towards finding how it can be used to treat mental health conditions like PTSD. During sessions involving MDMA, you don't feel as threatened by your trauma as you typically would while reliving it with your therapist.

The therapist provides you with a comfortable and calm space to process your trauma without any pressure, judgment, or fear. Since you don't feel any fear or danger with the help of MDMA, it is easy to process the emotions and thoughts associated with the event.

Choosing a Therapist

When in search of a therapist to help with your treatment, look for mental health experts who specialize in treating PTSD and trauma.

You can also reach out to a counseling center, local mental health clinic, counseling center, or psychiatric hospital for referrals.

In addition to experience and credentials, it is crucial to look for therapists who make you feel secure and comfortable. You are going to be letting out what you feel, and someone who has these traits will make things easier.

Lastly, trust your instincts. If you don't feel right with a therapist, you should not ignore that feeling. Instead, let them be and find someone else.

How to Access Treatment

There are various treatment options available for PTSD, and the numbers will likely increase later in the future as technology advances. But knowing about these treatment options is only a step, as you will still have to determine how to access them.

Below are a few of the easiest ways to get the treatment you need:

The Internet

The internet is a comprehensive source of information and can help connect you to resources around you. There are numerous online platforms like PTSD Alliance that can help you find treatment programs close to you that are certain to meet your specific requirements.

Your Doctor

Reaching out to your doctor can be a good way to start searching for the right treatment. Many physicians, health experts, and doctors have a strong network and will certainly be able to link you up with a good therapist for your condition.

When it comes to treating PTSD, there is no right or wrong strategy available. Every individual differs, and some people are more responsive to specific kinds of treatments than others.

The efficiency of a specific treatment is dependent on a variety of factors like:

- The seriousness of the symptoms.

- The type of trauma.

- The availability of a support network.

- The personality of the individual.

Lastly, even though there are numerous kinds of treatments available for PTSD, there are some which have been known to provide more positive outcomes than others.

Self-help Treatment Options

Some people may choose to use other alternatives instead of the treatment options and alternative treatment options available for PTSD. These are self-help techniques, and they can be effective in dealing with PTSD triggers. Below are a few of the common ones you can try out.

Meditation

Meditation can teach you how to be more aware of the now and operate with mindfulness. When you practice mindfulness, you develop an awareness of all your thoughts, feelings, and body sensations. You also learn the triggers of your PTSD so you can better manage them.

Meditation can also help you deal with the inconvenient memories and thoughts associated with your trauma. This can let you overcome them without any judgment.

Research has also proven that meditation is beneficial for PTSD. Researchers studied the use of guided meditation to treat veterans with PTSD. After the veterans participated in weekly meditations for a month, they experienced a drastic reduction in cortisol, which is the hormone responsible for stress.

Meditation was proven to work more efficiently for PTSD than the standard treatment options.

Remain Active

Working out when you have PTSD can be very beneficial for you. Exercise helps to enhance your mood and can help you deal with symptoms of PTSD like irritability and anxiety.

Physical activity can also help you stay happy and offer you relief from the flashbacks and nightmares. You can also take these benefits further by joining a running group or a gym, as you can also get social support from these locations.

According to research, exercise has been proven to be ideal for individuals dealing with PTSD. Researchers found in a recent study that exercise reduces depression and other symptoms of PTSD.

Get a Pet

Pets can help you stay calm and offer you companionship if you are dealing with PTSD. Good options are service dogs and cats. Service dogs can easily be accessed if you reach out to organizations like the Service Dogs for America and pets for vets. These organizations can tell you all you need to know about how to get a service dog for PTSD.

Service dogs for America will let you send in applications for service dogs and will accept them from anyone who has PTSD. The great news is that you don't have to be in the military to enjoy this benefit. This organization can train dogs to learn and note the signs of PTSD like nightmares and anxiety. They are also taught to assist you when you experience these symptoms.

PTSD service dogs can assist and provide support in various ways. For instance, if you are experiencing a nightmare, they may paw at you to help you wake up. They can also be trained to bring medications, offer distractions, or let others know that you are in distress.

Establish Boundaries

If you are battling with PTSD, it is undoubtedly going to affect your family and friends in one way or another. It can be challenging to handle your relationships and deal with PTSD simultaneously. It will be crucial to put boundaries in place in your relationships when dealing with PTSD.

When a person suffers from trauma like sexual assault or domestic violence, it is a violation of their boundaries. For this reason, you will need to speak about your PTSD triggers to your loved ones and friends and request that they give you time and space when you need it.

Individuals who have survived PTSD state that establishing boundaries and personal space are essential for minimizing anxiety. When a loved one refuses to provide someone with PTSD with the needed space when they need it, it may result in a feeling of danger. To ensure this does not happen, it is vital to let them know about your needs, as discussed above.

However, if someone crosses your boundary, you may need to let them know in a calm voice. Other times, it may be best to walk away from a situation when someone violates your boundaries.

Find A Creative Outlet

Creative outlets like music therapy and art therapy for PTSD can positively influence your symptoms. Other hobbies like crafting, creative writing, woodworking, sewing, cooking, journaling, and painting can offer respite from irritability and anxiety.

Besides, some experts suggest that creative tasks like art projects may be ideal for people who are unable to find the relief they require from the standard therapies.

This is also supported by research, which proves that creative therapies can work for PTSD. Researchers observed during a study of veterans that a music intervention drastically minimized the symptoms of depression. It also minimized the seriousness of PTSD.

Establish a Support System

Support systems are essential for everyone. They can be beneficial in getting past various circumstances, and mental health conditions are not excluded. Having people who are always willing to listen to you speak about your condition and challenges is crucial for recovery. These could include your coworkers, loved ones, or friends. This network of people will be available to provide you with solutions during those periods you are stuck.

People who have dealt with numerous traumatic events will find that a social support system is hugely beneficial to them. A study observed that the possibility of attaining PTSD was 17 times more likely in women who had experienced both rape and child abuse. However, the severity of PTSD was less in those who had access to more social support. In essence, having social support can ease some of the symptoms of this disorder.

Aromatherapy

This practice involves the use of essential oils to deal with ailments, which range from depression to headaches. It could consist of inhaling, diffusing, rubbing on the skin, or consuming oils. For PTSD, aromatherapy may consist of essential oils like lavender, rose, and sage, which are recognized for their calming properties.

It is believed that aromatherapy provides a calming effect, which means it will be ideal for the treatment of PTSD symptoms like distress and worry. What's more, essential oils could help in dealing with sleep disruptions in individuals experiencing PTSD.

Five Stages of Recovery

To get the treatment you desire, you will need to go through the stages of recovery. By the time you get to the last stage, you will be well on your way to getting the recovery you seek.

These stages are discussed below.

The Emergency Stage

This is the stage where everything is heightened. Your levels of anxiety and your response to everything in your surroundings will be powerful. It is at this point where your body might go into the fight or flight mode due to the hypersensitivity and feelings of danger. This is what opens you up for the next stage.

The Numbing Stage

Here, you will do everything possible to safeguard yourself from experiencing more mental misery. It will be at this point that you avoid or deny the emotions that you are feeling.

Most times, your mind tries to deal with the intense emotions you are feeling by avoiding them. However, this is only a temporary solution. If you don't get the right treatment for your PTSD, you may be stuck in this stage.

The Intrusive/Repetitive Stage

In most cases, you will realize that regardless of the effort you put into avoiding your emotions, you only feel worse. The intensity of the flashbacks and nightmares increase, and you don't stop feeling like you are in danger. This will result in you feeling jumpy and nervous.

This stage is one of the deadliest of all the stages as it can cause the most damage. However, it is also at this point that you can confront the trauma that is taking charge of your life.

The Transition Stage

As the name implies, during this stage you start to move into a new level of understanding. You begin to accept what happened and the influence it has had on your life. Healing begins from this point, as soon as you have accepted your trauma.

You start to look at your life from another perspective and develop a better idea of how you can deal with your PTSD for good.

The Integration Stage

You get to this stage when you have successfully completed aspects of your PTSD recovery. You find out strategies to help you get over your PTSD symptoms, and start to incorporate the skills into your life to help you function as normal and move forward.

It is not easy to get to this stage; you will need to be committed and do the work. Sometimes you may slip and make mistakes, but it is crucial that you don't dwell on them but instead see them as lessons. Also, remember to keep all you have learned close by during your treatment.

Chapter 3:

Write Your Way to Freedom

Writing, in general, is highly beneficial. It can help clear your thoughts and act as an outlet for your emotions. If you can incorporate it into your life, the results will be outstanding for those who have PTSD.

One way to make writing a habit in your life is through journaling. This simple process offers people with PTSD numerous benefits that can help their recovery. This chapter will cover all you need to know about journaling and the benefits it offers.

What is Journaling, and How Can It Help?

Journaling is the process of writing down your thoughts and how you feel. It is an excellent means to keep tabs on your daily life and determine what makes you happy and upset.

Keeping a journal can help you create a meaningful connection with yourself. Having this sort of connection is as significant as building relevant connections with your friends and loved ones.

Journaling can improve the quality of your life and help you achieve any objectives you can have. Everyone's journal may differ; however, the outcome is always beneficial. A journal can also help you keep your mind clear and make relevant connections between your feelings, thoughts, and the way you act.

Lastly, a journal can cushion or minimize the impact of mental conditions, including PTSD.

How Can Journaling Improve Your Mental Health?

You may believe journaling only involves writing down words in a book. So how exactly does it improve your mental health?

Surprisingly, this straightforward practice can offer numerous benefits like those listed above. However, it is even more beneficial for people dealing with mental conditions that are seeking to improve their mental health.

When using the journal method, you are exercising the left side of your brain, which is the more rational and analytical side. When your left hemisphere is busy, your right hemisphere, which is the creative side, has the opportunity to play. When this happens, your creativity thrives, which can make a significant difference in your daily life.

Journaling has been observed to:

- Improve your working memory.

- Enhance your mood.

- Improve your sense of well-being.

- Minimize symptoms of depression.

- Minimize avoidance symptoms.

Various theories propose that writing can help to improve mental health by urging you to confront those emotions you previously repressed. This can help you better process traumatic events and create a clear narrative about what you experienced.

Journaling can also be helpful for those who have no traumatic experience. It can improve their mental health by making them self-aware. When this happens, they can pinpoint those unhealthy behaviors and thought patterns. As a result, individuals can move from a negative mindset to one with more positivity.

However, you need to establish a steady writing process to receive the full benefits of journaling. Just mindlessly filling up your journal with words may help you feel good, but there is little to prove that it will help enhance your overall well-being.

Keep the following aspects of journaling in mind to ensure you write your journal the right way:

Use the Right Tool for You

Ideally, it's best to write with your own hands on a paper. However, with the advent of technology, there are a lot of other options available to you if handwriting is not your thing. You can use your laptop, phone, or tablet.

Observe Where You Are Presently

You will need to write down your present life situation. Write down everything you feel about your present living conditions. The better the understanding you have about these conditions, the easier it would be for you to start and determine your goal.

To begin, simply write everything that you can think of. Reflecting on your life can be highly beneficial to you and can be significant in finding solutions to your issues.

Write Each Day

After you have determined where your life is, you can then begin writing regularly. Write anything you can think of for no less than two minutes. You are free to invest more time if you want, but ensure you are consistent.

You can write about things that trigger you or how you feel. Regardless of which option you choose to go with, make certain you do it regularly. Once you write in your journal each day, it will soon become a habit. When this happens, you can then invest more time into journaling.

If you observe that your consistency is starting to drop due to the time you are investing, you could reduce it to a more manageable time frame.

List Out Your Goals and Wins

Ensure you include all of your goals and successes in your journal. Writing down your accomplishments can give you that boost of positivity you desire. Like we discussed earlier, this is especially significant for anyone dealing with PTSD.

Have Your Journal Handy

Try to take your journal anywhere you go. This will enable you to write the things you feel at any time. It does not matter if you are traveling for a vacation or going on a business trip. Do all you can to keep it handy and be consistent with your writing.

Read Through Your Journal

Go through your journal frequently. Pick a comfortable schedule and stick to it. This journal review could happen weekly, monthly, or quarterly. Doing this will let you spot any changes that may have happened in your life. Look at the things that bother you the most and areas that you have improved.

How Journaling Helps PTSD Recovery

Journaling is a great way to find healing for any disorder, habit, or event that you are trying to get over.

If you are dealing with the effects of a traumatic event, you can use journaling to find the positive aspects of your life. This can help minimize the symptoms that can come with trauma.

Avoidance symptoms can also be addressed through journaling. Seeing the issues you've been avoiding written down can help you stop avoiding them. This can encourage you to confront them head-on, which can bring about relief down the road.

If you have the opposite problem and intrusion symptoms cause you to constantly think about your trauma, journaling can help you get these thoughts out of your head, so you stop constantly worrying about them. This can free up your mind, help you deal with stress, and manage your emotions.

Also, if you are looking to recover from any traumatic event which has left you heartbroken, like the death of a loved one, journaling can help. Writing down your thoughts can help you process what has happened and minimize the feeling of guilt and loss.

Journaling can help you see your accomplishments. These small wins can be ideal for improving your mental health when dealing with PTSD.

But that is not all. Journaling can help you deal with some core symptoms of PTSD, which are anxiety, stress, and emotions.

Journaling and Anxiety

Journaling is beneficial for people experiencing anxiety disorders like depression. Barbara Markway, a psychologist, stated that to deal with our challenging thought patterns, it is essential to first know what they are.

Journaling can help you point out all of the negative automatic self-talk you are dealing with and get to the source of your anxiety.

Writing in a journal can influence your anxiety positively by:

- Freeing and calming your mind.

- Helping you release negative thoughts which may be due to your PTSD.

- Improving your self-awareness.

- Informing you about your triggers.

- Helping you monitor your progress during recovery.

Journaling and Stress

If you are dealing with stress as a result of your PTSD, journaling can be an excellent method to help you manage it. This will ensure you don't fall into depression or anxiety.

With a journal, you can release tension and be one with your emotions. It can also aid you in minimizing stressors in your life or achieving a crucial goal.

Journaling can help you deal with stress by:

- Enhancing your cognitive functioning.

- Exploring your thoughts and moving your perspective to something less stressful.

- Promoting self-awareness and urging action.

Journaling and Your Emotions

Journaling has been observed to help individuals clear emotions. As you must know, PTSD can have a massive impact on how you feel, and journaling can help you keep things calm. It does this through the following:

- Enhancing focus.

- Providing more stability.

- Allowing you to let go of the past.

- Minimizing the disorderliness in your life.

- Giving you the chance to become one with your thoughts and change them.

When you are extremely emotional, journaling can allow you to understand these emotions. The instant you have put down everything you are feeling in your journal, you will find peace, become more objective, and can move forward.

When there is no journal, you can be stuck with crippling emotions from your trauma for a long time. However, journaling genuinely and consistently can be one of the best routes to recovery. With time, you will begin to function in society once more properly.

Steps to Start Journaling

- Look for a quiet location with minimal distractions. Schedule some time each day with the least distractions. However, even if there is a bit of noise, it should not be a problem. Some individuals can do well in noisy environments, or even during short breaks. All you need to do is pick a location that is ideal for you.

- Take a few minutes to consider how your trauma or PTSD has influenced you and those around you.

- Start by putting down your deepest feelings and thoughts as regards the trauma you have experienced. If you can, invest no less than 20 minutes. However, it is not compulsory, as any amount of time you can invest will be adequate.

- The moment you are through writing, read what you put down, and note the way it makes you feel. Observe any change to your feelings and thoughts due to what you have written down.

- Even though journaling does offer you benefits, writing about your trauma can cause you distress. This is understandable, and it is nothing to worry about. All you need to do is ensure you have a plan to deal with these feelings when they do arise.

- Repeat the steps above and write on the same topic for two days more. It has been observed that writing about the same subject during consecutive days can help improve thought clarity. It can also improve the feelings you have about a stressful situation.

Other Tips That Could Help Ease the Process

Don't pay attention to grammar or spelling. All you need to do is pay attention to letting out all of your feelings and thoughts.

When writing, try to be comprehensive in your writing. For instance, when describing how you felt, write out the thoughts associated with those feelings and the precise way they felt in your body.

For instance: "My head hurt" or "My skin felt chilly."

This will help enhance your awareness and the clarity of your thoughts and emotions.

Ideally, you should keep your journal close so you can always go through it to see how your feelings and thoughts have changed over the years. However, if you don't want someone finding your journal and going through what you have written, make certain that you find a secure means of storing them.

Even though it may be best to invest some time into writing each day to enable you to stay consistent as covered above, you are allowed to be flexible. Anytime something that causes you stress happens in your life, you are free to write down your feelings even if it does not align with your schedule.

Journaling Prompts to Help You Out

If you don't know where to begin or feel stuck, here are a few prompts to help you:

- Try to be as detailed as you can when writing about your trauma. Try to cover how it made you feel physically and emotionally.

- What are the lessons you picked up from the experience? Write them all out. It does not matter if they are good or bad.

- What impact does the experience have on your life presently? As usual, be elaborate when doing this.

- Are there things you hoped you could change or do differently? If yes, why do you want to change them?

- List out some of the major things that bring stress in your life presently. Did this change after you experienced your trauma? If yes, is it possible to point out the reason why this is?

- Did your experience affect those around you? This could either be people in your life presently, or those who used to be around.

- If there is anything you feel you should have shown more gratitude for before the trauma, what would it be? Or is there anything you would like to have back?

- Are there lessons you could teach others from your experience?

As you can see, journaling can do a lot to help out with your PTSD. Whip out that journal and begin writing down your thoughts today. But there is something that is just as important as journaling; you need to have self-awareness.

Chapter 4:

Self-Awareness

Self-awareness is a simple term. It means being aware of the self. But what exactly is the meaning of this? And how can it help with PTSD? As straightforward as this term may be, it is still incredibly complex.

Many people lack this ability and don't even know how to go about getting it. Still, it is a great way to get peace from all the disorganized emotions that come from PTSD.

We will be uncovering all of this in this chapter, but first, let us start with a comprehensive definition of this term.

What is Self-Awareness

Self-awareness means having a conscious knowledge about your feelings and character. Many individuals navigate through life without really being aware of our actions and the reason behind them.

This may not be a bad thing since it is easier when we run on autopilot without having to think about every detail. However, it becomes a problem when we stop realizing some of our more important actions.

Our minds quickly form a pattern of emotional responses, so it is very easy for specific responses to transform into habits. When you are self-aware, you are conscious of this fact. This means you can take charge of your emotional responses, particularly the unhealthy ones.

Self-Awareness Examples

On the surface, self-awareness is being conscious of your actions. However, if you go deeper, it has to do with identifying the problems you deal with due to your actions and finding techniques to correct them.

Awareness of Actions

The initial phase of self-awareness involves being aware of your actions and, most importantly, how you distract yourself.

For instance, how often do you turn on your laptop to watch a few videos for a couple of minutes on YouTube, only to find out that you have spent hours doing so?

To distract ourselves from the pain we deal with in our daily lives; we often carry out passive actions without realizing what we are doing. This does not mean it is terrible to have distractions. They can help us deal with boredom. However, the problem arises when you allow these distractions to take charge of your life.

The instant you are aware of your distractions, it is a sign that you are on the right path.

Awareness of Feelings

The moment you have stopped using your distractions as a coping mechanism, you will most likely come across some feelings that you have been pushing downwards for some time. Some of these feelings could be anger, guilt, shame, and resentment.

It is crucial to become aware of these emotions because they will let you challenge the reasons behind them and probably look for a solution. Are you angry with your kids because they are playing roughly, or you have some underlying emotions caused by something else?

The moment you can point out the origin of your emotion, you should let it go and move on if possible. This way, you will understand the source of this feeling when it next comes up, and it won't affect you as much.

Why is Self-Awareness Essential?

If you want to improve your overall life, you will need to be self-aware. Since PTSD can leave you with many deep-rooted feelings and fears, it will be essential to be self-aware.

This is because self-awareness can help you manage all of your behaviors, emotions, and thoughts proactively, so they don't take control of your life.

If you are self-aware enough to understand your triggers and how they can affect you, it will be easy to determine how to deal with them and prevent them from negatively influencing your life.

Also, being fully aware of your feelings and actions will help you understand those around you better, which can help you develop better relationships. Being self-aware is a massive leap toward improving your life and freeing yourself from PTSD.

But even with all of these benefits, it is difficult for many people to be self-aware.

Why is it Difficult to be Self-Aware?

Many of us find it hard to be self-aware because we don't take note of what is going on within or around us. In most cases, when we run on auto mode, our mind drifts elsewhere instead of where we currently are.

Apart from this, it stops us from correctly understanding ourselves. Instead, we believe any narrative that is in line with what we already think even if it is not real.

Self-awareness, by its own nature, needs to be developed from the inside-out.

How to Foster Self-Awareness

Here are a few tips that can help cultivate self-awareness in your life:

Keep a Journal

By now, you probably know how powerful writing is for PTSD in general. But writing also helps you connect with yourself and gives you much-needed peace. It also enables you to free up your mind as you let out your thoughts.

Establish Some Space for Yourself

Imagine you are in a box. If you are stuck in this box, your line of sight will be limited. This means you will be unable to see things clearly. If you open the box even a little, the light will be able to come through.

When you create some space for yourself, it is similar to opening the box. You begin to see things more clearly.

Try to give yourself some time and space each day. This could be the moment you wake up or some minutes before you sleep. During this period, you will avoid any form of digital distractions and spend some time alone. This means turning off the television, switching off your phones, and staying away from the internet.

Instead, enjoy your own company by meditating, writing, or reading and build a connection with yourself.

Practice Mindfulness

Being mindful is one of the best ways to get self-awareness. It involves being in the present without any judgment. When you are mindful, you make yourself available to know what is going on within you and around you.

There are various ways to practice mindfulness. This could be through mindful walking, mindful eating, or mindful listening.

Mindfulness urges you to pay attention to yourself and stay in the present purposely. Next time something bothers you, leverage mindfulness to listen to yourself and learn the thoughts going on in your mind and how you are feeling.

By being present to acknowledge your emotions and feelings, you will soon become better at being self-aware.

Request Feedback

Asking others around you for feedback is something that never fails. There are instances feedback may not be accurate or sometimes dishonest and biased. However, the more you listen to feedback, the better you will become at separating biased feedback from genuine advice.

According to research, carrying out 360-degree feedback in the work environment is useful for improving the self-awareness of managers. It is impossible for us to see ourselves from all perspectives, so getting feedback can help you see those things you don't see.

If you only look within yourself, it may not be possible to get complete and genuine awareness. Getting perspectives from various people can help you see a complete picture of yourself.

Practice the Art of Listening

Good listening is an art that not everyone has perfected. However, it is a skill that can help you become self-aware. While listening, you should pay attention to the emotions and body language of others. Give them your understanding without any form of judgment.

The moment you perfect the art of listening to others, you will also learn to listen to yourself better and stay connected with your needs.

Ask "What?" instead of "Why?"

In most cases, when people look into their present environment and emotion, the major question they ask is, "Why?" For instance, why does this make me feel this way? Why is my business not going how I want?

According to research, asking why does not work because you don't have access to most of your unconscious feelings, motives, and thoughts.

There is a huge chance that you are wrong about why you think specific things, or about how you behave. For instance, if you get the feedback you don't like from a superior and think it's because you are not experienced enough. It is impossible for you to evaluate your weaknesses and strengths without any bias and come to the right conclusion.

Research has also proven that individuals who self-examine themselves have a higher tendency to use negative thoughts. Examining or evaluating yourself using "Why" questions can lead to depression and anxiety, which makes them ineffective.

Self-aware individuals ask "What" instead of "Why." Asking "What" questions pays attention to future goals and objectives as opposed to previous objectives.

For example, let us presume you are feeling down at home. "Why am I feeling this way?" will only leave you feeling more misery, which will force you to focus on the negative aspects.

Instead, asking a question like "What are the things at work that make me feel terrible?" urges you to notice factors beyond your control that don't fall in line with your goals and passions. It also aids you in creating strategies to help you correct those issues.

Dealing with Negative Thoughts

Because PTSD symptoms can be hard to deal with, numerous individuals dealing with this condition may battle with low self-esteem. This makes it crucial that they find out ways to enhance their self-image.

What's more, people who have PTSD may also experience depression, which may lead to them growing numerous negative thoughts about themselves. This could lead to a feeling of worthlessness and low self-esteem. Due to this, it is essential that you learn how to point out these thoughts and replace them with positive ones instead.

In doing this, you can provide yourself with the support you require. So, how do you get this done? The first step is to recognize your negative thoughts. It can be difficult to recognize negative thinking patterns. However, self-monitoring can be a great way of enhancing the awareness of your thoughts and how they can affect your behaviors and mood.

Reducing Your Negative Thoughts

It can be difficult to free yourself from negative thoughts. They tend to get stuck in your mind and grow from there. The more you pay attention to negative thoughts, the more powerful they become. The same also applies when you try to change these thoughts forcefully.

Instead of this, you may want to find healthy distractions that would help keep you away from them. There are numerous healthy distraction techniques like self-soothing, deep breathing, and mindfulness.

Remember that these distraction techniques may not eradicate these thoughts. Nonetheless, they may help you minimize how intense they are, which will make it easier for you to handle.

Challenging Your Thoughts

After you have minimized the intensity of your negative thoughts, the next step would be for you to challenge them.

Most negative thoughts stem from our insecurities. They are usually hardly real, but we believe they are and never really question them when they come. We only accept them.

To correct this, you need to challenge these thoughts. These questions can help you do this:

- What evidence is available to show that this thought is real?

- What evidence do I have that shows that it is not?

- Are there instances when this thought has turned out to be false?

- Do these kinds of thoughts come up when I am feeling downcast as opposed to when I feel nervous, miserable, or sad?

- What would I say to another person who experiences these kinds of thoughts?

- What could be the explanation for this thought?

Positive Self-Supportive Statements

To further deal with negative thoughts, you can use positive self-supportive statements. For instance, you can write down all of your good qualities or things you have accomplished. You can also let yourself know that it is fine to be anxious.

You may also list some of the positive changes you have made in your life recently.

Positive self-talk comes with numerous benefits such as reducing stress, improving relationships, and building resilience and confidence. It can also help combat anxiety and stress, which are two of the main symptoms of PTSD.

How Positive Self-Talk Helps with Anxiety

Positive self-talk can help with problems like depression and anxiety. This is primarily because negative self-talk has been associated with conditions like anxiety, aggression, and PTSD.

It has been proven that if a person changes their self-talk from negative to positive, the outcome is very beneficial, especially for those who have anxiety problems.

In essence, positive-talk can help overcome all of these conditions, including PTSD. It does this by correcting the predisposition towards the negative thought pattern and beliefs of ourselves that we may have.

Positive Self-Talk and Stress

A major benefit of positive self-talk is that it can help you approach stressful circumstances and setbacks with a more positive and open mindset.

Positive self-talk simply involves you restructuring the way you see things, getting rid of negative bias, and going through life with the feeling that you can deal with various situations. And even if things do not turn out the way you want them to, the lessons you pick up will be beneficial to you in the future.

Examples of Positive Self-Talk Statements and Phrases

If you don't know what positive self-talk statements are, it can be hard to determine the right ones that may work for you. However, you need to recognize that everyone will have varying positive self-talk statements, and you may have to try out various ones to determine the one that works for you.

To begin, here are a few great positive statement options:

- I am relevant

- I am in complete control of my thoughts

- I have no control over what others think. I can only control me

- I have the power to change my thoughts and mind

- I will put in every effort possible to make certain this turns out well

- Although this was not the result I expected, I picked up a lot of lessons about myself.

- I am strong and can overcome this challenge

- I may not be there yet, but I am proud of my accomplishments so far

- This is a chance for me to pick up new lessons

- I can grow as an individual from the lessons I pick from this challenge

Using Positive Self-Talk

Before you start using positive self-talk, it will be crucial to determine the frequency of your negative thoughts, and the types of self-talk you are stuck with. The moment you fully understand this, you can begin changing your thoughts.

Most negative self-talk is usually one of the following:

- **Personalizing**: This is a situation where you blame yourself for everything that goes wrong.

- **Magnifying**: This implies you only pay attention to the negative things that take place in all situations while ignoring the positive aspects.

- **Polarizing**: People who have these kinds of negative thoughts see things as only good and bad. There is no middle ground or a gray area with this form of thinking.

- **Catastrophizing**: If you have this kind of negative thinking pattern, you will always expect the worst in every situation.

It is possible to fall into one or numerous categories of negative thinking. But as soon as you start to categorize your thoughts, you can then start replacing them with positive ones.

Note that this will require time, and it is not something that will happen in a single day. You will have to put in the effort and stay committed if you are serious about changing your negative self-talk.

That being said, some strategies can help you make this process easier.

Determine your Self-Talk Triggers

Some circumstances may trigger you to engage in negative self-talk at a higher frequency. For instance, you may observe that your negative self-talk arises when you play a musical instrument in front of an audience.

Noting these triggers can help you prepare yourself better and replace these negative self-talks with positive ones.

Leverage Positive Affirmations

Positive affirmations are a great way to address a negative self-image. Practice positive affirmations before you find yourself in a situation that will result in negative self-talk.

You can say them in front of the mirror each day when you wake and before you go to bed. This practice will soon become a habit, and you will start to believe it. To take things further, you can incorporate visuals along with your positive affirmations.

Write your favorite positive affirmations on small-sized papers and stick them around your home. You can stick them on the refrigerator, your door, or your bed stand. Reading these affirmations as you move around your home can fill you with more positivity.

Below are a few examples of amazing positive affirmations to try out:

- I am not a failure

- I am a confident and excellent individual

- I am confident in my capacity

Try to use the momentum from the examples above in creating positive affirmations that will be ideal for your situation.

Note How You Feel Frequently

Over time we tend to start believing our own negative thoughts, which makes changing to positive self-talk extremely tedious. This may result in one or two slips and mistakes before you find your way back.

Anytime you come across an obstacle, be sure to check in with your inner self to ensure your thoughts are not back to being negative. If you check and it has reverted, you can correct it with some positive phrases or affirmations.

Establish Boundaries

There may be instances when people around us bring negativity into our lives. Identifying these kinds of individuals will be vital as they are examples of negative self-talk triggers. If there is anyone who urges you to see yourself in a negative line, you may want to establish some strong boundaries. This will help ensure they are unable to rub off their negativity on you any longer.

And instead of being around these types of people, try to surround yourself with people who encourage you and bring positivity in your life.

Positive self-talk statements are an important aspect of the PTSD healing process. However, it can be hard to create positive statements when you are not in the right frame of mind. To curb this, you may want to write them on a small piece of paper that can fit in your pocket or purse. Anytime you feel down, all you need to do is take this paper out and read these positive statements.

Read these statements anytime you get the chance and not just when you are unhappy. Positive statements can serve as a preventative measure to avoid falling into negativity. It may take some time to get used to, but with practice, the positivity you've written down will soon become a part of you.

Remember that there will be positive statements and affirmations that won't match your personal experience. Try to find those that align with your situation and work with them. And lastly, remember that this is a process that may take time. Many of our negative thoughts started to develop since we were young. This means changing them won't be something that happens overnight.

Chapter 5:

Self-Care

Self-care is extremely crucial for anyone dealing with PTSD due to trauma. Trauma can cause a person's body to always remain in fight or flight mode, as we have covered earlier. That is why it is essential to engage in activities that can help the body relax and get out of this fearful state. This can be achieved through self-care.

When you can let go of this trauma, you can then start your journey to complete recovery. Self-care also gives individuals the chance to cover all the aspects of healing, which are physical, emotional, social, and spiritual. This is what makes it one of the core foundations for getting complete recovery.

Self-care has to do with caring for oneself. If your life is lacking one of the healing aspects, then self-care is doing all you can to bring it back to shape.

Self-care simply means you are taking care of your needs. It is a key part of living a balanced life, and even though many people understand this, it is something that is usually easily ignored.

It is a relevant part of life and even more critical when you are dealing with PTSD. After a traumatic event, good self-care strategies can have a lot of influence on how complete our recovery is.

Self-care does not look the same to everybody, because we all have varying needs.

Nonetheless, there are a few general strategies that can be used by anyone who wants to incorporate self-care in their lives.

Self-Care Techniques For PTSD

Sleep is vital for helping you deal with PTSD symptoms in the right manner. If you rest properly, there is a lower likelihood of you experiencing frustrations and stress during your day that can trigger negative thoughts.

Ideally, adults should get no less than seven to nine hours of sleep each night to stay in great shape. This can be influenced by the environment too. For starters, it is best to sleep in a completely dark room with a comfortable temperature.

Another way to ensure quality sleep is to make sure that you use a high-quality mattress. It is best to purchase a mattress that has excellent support and aligns with your preferred method of sleeping. If your bed is beyond 10 years of age, it may be time for a change as it will likely not give you the support you need for quality sleep any longer.

Find Support

Many people are of the notion that getting help makes you weak and powerless. However, this is far from the truth. When you get help, it is a sign that you recognize your capacity. Sharing what you have been through with others in the same situation can be very therapeutic.

If you are having problems dealing with the symptoms of PTSD, locating a skilled mental health expert who knows these symptoms can go a long way. This, combined with looking for a support group consisting of people dealing with similar problems, can be incredibly refreshing.

With the support of a mental health expert, you can deal with all of your trauma triggers and choose the right coping strategies.

Find a Healthy Physical Outlet

Trauma does not only have an influence on our minds but our bodies as well. For this reason, you must look for a physical outlet to let out all of the pent-up emotions. With trauma comes rage, pain, misery, guilt, and grief. All of these feelings combining and continually gnawing at you can leave you feeling numb.

This is why a healthy physical outlet to channel all of these feelings can be of help. Boxing, running, kickboxing, and weightlifting are all great options. You can listen to some positive affirmations or upbeat music as you do any of these activities.

You should choose an activity that you are comfortable with. The result may be the opposite of what you expect if you force yourself to do something that your body can't handle or wears you down.

Breathe

Mindful breathing exercises are an excellent way for people to manage their PTSD symptoms. Taking some time to breathe for a few minutes or hours each day, mindfully can offer positive results. It can help in regulating emotions and dealing with your frustrating triggers.

Meditation alters your brain so you can mindfully approach any reactions that could leave you trapped in trauma. Anyone can start engaging in meditative practices without any prior experience.

For a good and easy mindful breathing exercise you can use anywhere follow the steps below:

- Sit upright and close your eyes while trying to take in everything in your environment

- Then, breathe in as deeply as you can and feel your chest rise. Try to feel the air on your skin and lungs while you do this

- Next, let out all of the air and repeat the process for as many times as you like. When you are done, open your eyes and enjoy the relief that comes with it

Exercise

This is important to PTSD recovery as the right kind of exercise program can help you reduce the symptoms of PTSD. This is possible because it helps improve sleep and reduces your level of anxiety and depression.

However, you need to be cautious when choosing an exercise program. While some might be ideal for your specific condition, others may act as triggers depending on your personal experience.

Nonetheless, with the help of your therapist, or trauma-sensitive trainers, you can choose a workout program that is ideal for you.

Eat Healthily

Even though it might seem more fun to drink a lot of soda and eat sugary snacks, it can hurt your health in the long run. Instead, eat more whole foods, veggies, and other meals that will provide you with strength and energy. Try to see food only as a fuel source for your body.

You need to note that the kind of food you consume influences your energy levels, mood, and overall quality of life. Eating healthy can be the significant difference between a life filled with sickness, and a healthy and energetic one. This makes it one of the most vital self-care tips anybody can incorporate in their lives.

Begin Each Day with A Glass of Water

According to the Institute of Medicine, it is recommended that every individual drink no less than 10 cups of water daily. However, many of us fall short here, with people drinking as few as two cups of water daily and sometimes less.

This means many of us are leaving ourselves unknowingly dehydrated each day. When you are dehydrated, you feel mentally and physically worn out. It can also affect your functionality and make you irritable throughout the day.

Dehydration can also leave you susceptible to dizziness and headaches, which can be extremely dire when combined with your pre-existing PTSD symptoms.

To avoid all of this, it is best to stay hydrated by drinking more water. Try to drink less alcohol, coffee, fruit juice, and other sugary drinks. Crystal clear water is the best way to achieve the best results.

Take a New Class

Taking a new class that is out of your comfort zone can give you a significant boost of positivity. Regardless of if it is a gym class or music class, the result is the same. Your brain flourishes on new challenges similar to other parts of your body.

Learning a new skill, taking a new class, or learning a new language are examples of activities that can make your brain thrive. You may also consider engaging in yoga to encourage better sleep, improve breathing, and strengthen your immune system.

Pamper Yourself

This implies that you do something out of the ordinary for yourself that makes you feel relaxed and unique. Regardless of if a self-care massage, or pedicure, or even a meal at your favorite restaurant makes you feel good, go for it.

Whenever you take some time out of your busy schedule to take care of yourself and do something that makes you feel amazing, you are on the right track. This is because that is what self-care is majorly about.

Move More

We all know how important working out is, especially when it comes to staying in shape. However, not everyone can take out the time from their busy schedule to do this. Still, it is recommended that you engage in some form of physical activity every day.

This does not necessarily mean you should achieve it in the gym. Instead, it could be something as simple as doing chores, going for a walk, or taking a run.

Moving more offers tons of benefits to your health like encouraging weight loss, enhancing productivity and memory, and reducing your possibility of getting heart issues, stroke, and diabetes.

Staying active is a crucial aspect of each day because it aids in supporting a healthy body and mind. If you have problems choosing the right way to move, here are a few fantastic options:

- Go dancing! Turn up your favorite tune and let yourself go. This could be in your home alone or out dancing with friends

- Clean your home windows, or do some deep cleaning. This is a fantastic way to move around without having to leave your home

- Play a game that encourages you to move and dance. Some games, like the video game Just Dance, let you do this right from your home

- Ride a bike around your neighborhood

Assist Others

Assisting others can be an excellent means of engaging in self-care. Whether you choose to frequently volunteer each month, donate to charity, or help out a neighbor in need, the results remain the same. You can make a huge difference to yourself and those around you.

Say No

A great self-care activity many people tend to have problems is knowing when to say no. if you feel like you are always saying yes to people that ask you for a favor, then it could be a huge problem. Even though it is rewarding to help out others when you can, if you notice your calendar is always full, you will need to learn to say no.

If you feel you are tied down and exhausted, take some downtime to rejuvenate. Cut down on how often you say yes, and ensure you are only taking up only activities or requests that you are comfortable with. Agreeing to and doing only things you are passionate about can offer you huge benefits.

Find Some Hobbies

Developing new hobbies is a great self-care strategy. There are many hobbies to choose from, including:

- Writing

- Gardening

- Art

- Photography

- Knitting

- Woodwork

These are only a few examples. There are tons of hobbies you can leverage. All you need to do is find something you have an interest in.

Self-Soothing and How It Can Help

This is the capacity to calm and comfort ourselves after we deal with a stressful event. Self-soothing is a tool we can use to keep ourselves calm when distressed or dealing with anxiety without the need for medications or other negative coping mechanisms. It has to do with showing kindness and comfort to yourself.

The following strategies can help you out, particularly if you are dealing with PTSD and anxiety.

Self-Holding

This simply means hugging yourself. This is a practice that was put together by Peter Levine to calm the nervous systems. It is no news that hugs trigger the release of oxytocin, which is a feel-good hormone. However, what you may not know is that self-hugs provide the same benefits. So, anytime you feel down, find a quiet space, and hug yourself while letting the feelings sink in.

Gentle Hand Technique

Anytime you are feeling down, close your eyes and pay attention to your body. Focus on that part of your body you feel the most discomfort and place a gentle hand on that area. This is similar to the way a mother would hold on to her child. Hold that area and pay attention to your hand resting over your fear calmly. After a few minutes, you will observe that your anxiety and fear are reducing.

Cross Your Arms and Do Some Deep Breathing

When experiencing PTSD symptoms, you may feel broken and fractured. When in this state, it is not easy to remain in your body. When something that triggers all of these symptoms occurs, this technique can be of help. Crossing your arms makes you feel safe, and rocking gives you the feeling of being in the hands of a loving parent. This, combined with deep breathing, is an excellent form of self-soothing.

Move Your Body

When you deal with any stressor, your body goes into the fight or flight mode, which generates a huge amount of energy. To get rid of some of this surplus energy, you will need to move your body. The tips we discussed earlier can help you out.

Buy a Weighted Blanket

Poor sleep pattern is something that often comes with PTSD. If you have this kind of problem, a weighted blanket may be an ideal investment. These blankets apply deep touch pressure stimulation (DTPS) squarely all over your body. In turn, this lets the happy chemicals in your brain know it's time to help you relax.

Use Some Herbs

There are numerous herbs out there that can help soothe you. A very common one is Tulsi tea. This is an adaptogenic herb which implies that it aids the body in adapting to stress. It is also known as holy basil because of its restorative and spiritual elements. This tea can also be used for headaches, depression, fatigue, and high blood pressure. All of these make it a great choice for self-soothing. Other good options include chamomile, damiana, and ginger tea.

Engage in Self-Massage

This is a self-soothing technique that can be fun if done right. When we are dealing with stress, our muscles contract as it is the body's way of going into fight or flight mode. However, when you are constantly in this mode, which is the case with people dealing with PTSD, it can begin to tell on your muscles.

In this situation, massaging your muscles can help loosen the tension, improve the circulation of blood, and rejuvenate your energy. Massages offer almost the same benefits as hugs by letting out hormones like serotonin and dopamine, which are both responsible for urging happiness.

Engaging in a self-massage is not difficult as the major tools you need are your hands. However, you can also invest in some massage tools like an electric massager or manual one.

Use Smells

Specific smells can offer us comfort and help in calming us when we are stressed, anxious, or nervous. There are various ways to create specific smells in your home or environment. You can use incense, candles, fabric conditioners, or specific meals. All of these can help us stay calm and relaxed in our living environment.

For instance, if you love the smell of roses and it helps you remain calm, there are ways to take it about with you. Purchase a rose essential oil and put a few drops on your palm or buy rose pouches, which you can place in your pockets or bag.

Use Taste

Tasting a snack can offer you something to focus on and provide a soothing effect. A great way of doing this is to chew gum. Studies have proven that chewing gum can help minimize levels of anxiety when dealing with high levels of stress.

Boiled sweets are also a great option as the taste and feeling that comes with sucking on them can help us remember calming times.

Use Warmth

Experiencing something warm can help us relax and feel calm. These could range from taking a warm bath or drinking some hot water or coffee. All of these can be great ways to soothe yourself and stay relaxed.

Reduce the Noise

The amount of noise in our environment can have an impact on our feelings. Some people enjoy complete silence because it allows the brain time to relax. Others may prefer to be around sound because this is the only way they can get their mind to relax.

However, many people will find themselves in between these two options. This means going with an environment that is not so quiet but not too noisy either. It should be noisy enough not to cause a distraction, but quiet enough to help your mind relax.

What we listen to also influences our feelings. Some people find upbeat music soothing, while others prefer slow music. Pick an option that works for you and practice self-soothing through audio when your mind feels like a wreck.

Use Apps

There are tons of apps created specifically to soothe you during moments of anxiety. Many of these apps can be of help from any location. Some of these include Acupressure, Headspace, and Stop Panic & Anxiety Self-Help.

In addition to these, some games can distract you while offering you calm like Paper.io or Flow Free.

Let it Out

There are moments when all we need is to let it out. This is particularly the case when all of our anxiety and emotions have built up over time. Crying is an excellent way to do this. Even though many people see crying as being weak, it is actually a natural way to soothe yourself. You can choose a quiet spot and let it out, and you will certainly feel much better.

Chapter 6:

PTSD and Relationships

PTSD can affect all the relationships of an individual. This could include their relationship with partners, family, friends, and even coworkers. In this chapter, we will be looking at how it affects each of these areas, and the steps you can take to make sure the impact is not severe on your life.

The National Center for PTSD states that individuals who have survived trauma and have PTSD often face issues in their family, intimate relationships, or friendships.

PTSD includes symptoms that affect emotional closeness, trust, problem-solving, and communication. Someone with PTSD may have increased feelings of disinterest in sexual and social activities. Also, individuals may deal with emotional numbness and feel isolated from others. All of these may result in partners, family members, and friends being distant and angry at the person with PTSD.

PTSD and Romantic Relationships

Individuals who have survived traumatic events like domestic violence, torture, physical and sexual abuse during childhood, terrorism often report feeling a sense of betrayal, horror, defenselessness, and fear that affects romantic relationships.

Due to their past trauma, individuals with PTSD may feel that it is dangerous to get too close or trust someone else. They may also feel that it is not safe to be sexually or emotionally intimate with other people.

Individuals who suffer PTSD due to trauma that involved violence and rage often battle with severe anger and other impulses. These individuals usually suppress these feelings by constantly criticizing friends and loved ones. They could also suppress it by ensuring they don't get too close to anyone. To effectively do this, there may be bouts of physical or verbal violence in intimate relationships.

As a means of coping with PTSD, some survivors may have an unhealthy dependence on family members, friends, or therapists. Some of them may also turn to substance and alcohol abuse as a coping mechanism for PTSD symptoms, all of which can cause havoc and even wreck friendships and relationships.

Nightmares, which are common in people who experience PTSD, may prevent both the individual and their partner from having a night of uninterrupted sleep. This may result in sleeping becoming problematic for both parties.

When an individual deals with PTSD, they may be hypersensitive, easily worried and anxious, unable to socialize, and always feeling irritable. In some cases, they may lack the capacity to be truly intimate with their partners, which can make intimacy more like a chore for both parties. All of these may result in partners feeling tense and pressured.

Avoiding trauma triggers and battling with anger and fear can affect the capacity of the person with PTSD to focus, listen, and make smart decisions. Due to this, issues may be left unresolved and continue to cause problems in the relationship. Also, partners may find it impossible to collaborate and communicate with the individual.

People with PTSD may experience flashbacks from their trauma, which can make them remain on edge at all times. This can make it difficult for partners of these individuals as it may result in them feeling like they have PTSD themselves.

How to Deal With PTSD in a Relationship

A successful relationship requires commitment, effort, and dedication. Communication and learning to express one's emotions and needs are crucial for relationships to be a success. You should also keep in mind the following practices to help make sure your relationship is a success.

Build a Good Support System

Many individuals dealing with PTSD have observed that developing a personal support network to deal with PTSD can be of help. It can also be helpful to broaden the already existing support network as a way to cope with PTSD.

Another aspect of a good relationship is every partner learning to share their feelings honestly and openly with compassion and respect. To develop this skill, alongside other skills that aid in strengthening communication, will require constant practice. Healthy relationships consist of relaxation, shared interests, and the enjoyment of each other's company.

Individuals who have PTSD can benefit from relationships with friends, family, and intimate relationships. This is because these offer them a place to belong, along with companionship as a means to deal with isolation, and eradicate guilt and depression.

Seek Treatment

Similar to all health issues that affect emotional and psychological functioning, the best option is to seek treatment from a professional health expert. This should be one who is skilled in treating PTSD and other family problems.

The majority of therapists with these skills are a part of the International Society for Traumatic Stress Studies (ISTSS). The membership directory of this group will list out all of the therapists who treat individuals with PTSD, couples, and family issues.

The kind of professional help that will be beneficial to you as a person experiencing PTSD trying to save your relationship will most often consist of couples or individual counseling. There are instances where group therapy may be included in counseling; however, this is dependent on the individual requirements and predicament of the person involved.

Numerous topics may be covered in therapy, which may range from stress management, anger management, parenting skills training, and communication skills training. The therapist will come up with a treatment plan that makes the most sense to the individual involved.

Use Medications if Prescribed

If your doctor prescribes medication to help you manage your condition, you should be sure to use them. It is for the benefit of you and your relationships. You are not going to be able to maintain or rebuild a relationship if you are not making conscious efforts to heal.

Share Your Feelings

Don't leave your partner guessing what you are going through. Do everything possible to make sure you fill them in and not leave them out of your life. This way, they understand what to expect and provide you with the support you need during trying times.

Integrate Fun and Playfulness Into Your Life

PTSD could result in one feeling miserable, sad, and angry. All of these can rub off on your partner and relationship. To maintain your relationship, it is suggested that you incorporate some fun and playfulness into your life. This will make you feel less miserable, and this will be evident in your relationship. Try to plan fun activities you and your partner can enjoy together. There is no better way to build closeness than this.

Find Out More About Your PTSD

If you want to maintain your relationship, you will need to determine your PTSD symptoms alongside the various triggers. All of these will be essential in teaching you all you need to know to manage the symptoms properly when they arise.

Deal with Any Problems of Substance Abuse

People who experience PTSD tend to use alcohol and other substances as coping mechanisms. These may provide temporary relief, but in the long run, they will hurt your family and health.

If your goal is to have a long-lasting and healthy relationship, it will be crucial for you to address any problems of alcohol and substance abuse that you may be experiencing.

Use Healthy Habits to Deal with your PTSD symptoms

There are many habits you can develop to help you deal with your triggers and PTSD symptoms when they arise. We have covered many of these earlier, but some helpful options include exercise, meditation, and mindful breathing. All of these can help you manage your symptoms, so they don't affect your relationship.

Connect with Individuals in your Shoes

Reaching out to other people dealing with PTSD can help you understand yourself and your condition better. It can be very refreshing to speak to those who are dealing with the same kind of situation. They may have other insights and tips that can help you maintain your relationships.

Partake in Couples and Individual Counseling Regularly

Counseling of any form can do wonders for you if you are experiencing PTSD. With couples counseling, you and your partner can share problem areas, find a solution to these problems, and build a healthier relationship. Many experienced therapists provide this form of service for couples.

You can also try out individual counseling, which can help you let your feelings out and find ways to maintain your relationship.

How to Communicate Relationship Needs

Like we have covered earlier, PTSD affects all of your relationships, including your family and friends. They will witness how you are responding to stressors and the outward signs of PTSD you display, which makes it essential to let them know what you are going through.

Sharing your feelings and what you are going through can be a difficult task. However, if you take the step, you will be able to connect in meaningful and profound ways. You will be able to meet your needs and have a healthier relationship.

Nonetheless, for many individuals, it can be extremely tasking to share your feelings. This is even worsened for people with PTSD who may feel scared of opening themselves to the possibility of being hurt once more. Still, if you do it right, it can be very beneficial and vital to your progress.

That being said, the strategies below can help you communicate your needs in an effective manner so that you can adequately put your friends and family in the loop.

Determine Your Feelings

Before communicating your feelings, it is vital to first determine what they are. People around you can't read your mind to understand the hurdles and problems you are experiencing.

Do you feel sad, angry, or frustrated? Make sure it is clear before you proceed. You need to be honest about these feelings. To do this, you can determine them on your own, or seek the help of a therapist or someone you trust before you decide to share these needs.

Pick a Good Time

What you say to someone is crucial. However, when you say it is also as vital. Your conversation may go how you expect if the person you are trying to talk to is in the best mood. If you decide to speak with your loved ones about what you are going through at the same moment they are dealing with problems of their own or are unhappy, you may not get the results you are after.

If you can, it's best to wait until everyone in the conversation is calm, and they all have the time for a serious talk. Waiting until something great has happened and everyone is in a light mood can be beneficial, but you shouldn't feel like you need to keep waiting for a perfect moment. It's generally best to lean towards expressing your emotions instead of keeping them to yourself. If you know a wedding may make your friends more receptive to discussing your PTSD in two months, you may be better off talking with them next week instead. Your therapist or a trusted loved one who knows what you're going through can be an invaluable asset to help you reach a timing decision that works best for you.

Be Calm

When talking about something that has caused you pain over the years, and has the tendency to make you angry or emotional, you need to approach it with caution.

When communicating your feelings and needs to your friends and loved ones, the chat can quickly become heated. This is especially the case if you don't get the support you expect or need.

In as much as it is understandable to feel hurt and resentful that your loved ones are refusing to meet your needs, you need to respect their decision if they say no.

You can't always get what you want. If they reject your request, try to see things from their perspective and understand instead of being resentful.

Share Only With Someone You Trust

Sharing your feelings means you are making yourself vulnerable and letting someone in. They are intimate aspects of yourself and not something you should share with a random person.

Proceed with caution when sharing. Start with those feelings that don't make you as vulnerable, and observe how they respond before you delve into the actual matter at hand.

Respond Don't React

There are instances when we want to communicate our feelings and make the mistake of rushing through the process. This results in us saying things before we had the opportunity to think it through.

It is not far-fetched to take a break from a conversation until we have finished with our thoughts. This is why it is advisable to first determine your feelings before you proceed into the actual discussion.

If you are having a hard time staying calm during a conversation, take a few minutes off and do something to help calm yourself before going back to the conversation.

Listen Properly

Communication is a two-way concept. As you express your feelings and needs, you will also need to understand the feelings of the other person. This can only be achieved if you listen and let whoever you are speaking to know that you are listening.

When the other party, or parties, involved in the conversation can tell you are listening, they will be more willing to share more and listen to what you have to say. There are many verbal cues you can use to show that you are listening to. You can nod to show that you are focused or say "yes" or "okay" frequently during the conversation.

Effective communication is something that needs a lot of practice and skill. Because of how differently people are built, you will need to learn to adjust to different people and their communication needs. Nonetheless, the strategies above are your best bet when you want to fill your friends and loved ones in on what you are dealing with.

Dealing with PTSD at the Workplace

PTSD can affect a person in the workplace too. When this happens, it may make it difficult for a person to stay focused and productive at work.

If you deal with a PTSD trigger at work, it can leave you feeling scared, anxious, irritable, nervous, and edgy. It may be difficult for you to remember important information, finishing up projects, properly managing your time, and interacting with other individuals in the workplace.

What's more, your mind may become clouded with upsetting memories, which can startle you and impact how you function at work. It can be difficult to properly do your job when all you are thinking of are the scary memories from your trauma.

Symptoms like depression, alcohol, and substance use, along with low mood, can keep you thinking of your trauma, and this may have an impact on how you do your job. In most cases, it is impossible to work at all with all of these lingering problems. This is also the same situation for many other people dealing with PTSD.

Still, some people may be able to function for a while. Their symptoms may not be as severe as others, and they may also have learned how to keep their negative thoughts to themselves over time. These types of individuals may face more problems at night or when they are alone.

However, if these individuals fail to get treatment, their symptoms will worsen, and they won't be able to function as they used to. Even these seemingly high-functioning people will be unable to keep a job for long.

There are a few ways you can return yourself to peak functionality, even at work. The strategies below can help you achieve this feat.

Find Out What Calms You

What helps you get calm? Determine the smells, sounds, sights, and sensations that can help tone down your symptoms. We covered how to do this in the earlier chapter. For some people, using essential oils like rose and lavender can offer the calm they need.

Others may prefer sounds, and things like soft music and water sounds can help. In other cases, a texture may be what helps you calm, while others may do well with meditation.

Look for what makes you feel good, and leverage it anytime you deal with a trigger at work.

Fill Your Workspace With Those Things You Love

When you genuinely love something, it can make you happy, elevate your mood, and help you stay calm. Try to place pictures of places and individuals you love the most around your workspace. Placing plants can also help.

Anytime we experience PTSD symptoms, all of our attention goes to the memories from our trauma. By rechanneling your focus to those things you love, it can bring you back into the moment, and away from the horrible memories.

Chant or Hum

Engaging in these forms of behaviors can trigger the vagus nerve. This is the nerve that goes from our brain down to our gut. It has an impact on our capacity to stay calm. This is because it is in charge of the body systems responsible for moving us out of the fight and flight mode.

Humming, chanting, and facial exercises can help calm your PTSD symptoms. These could be extremely beneficial when you are at work.

You can also try out some of the other tips we discussed earlier like:

- Chewing Gum

- Using an App

- Seeking professional help

Should You Tell Your Boss About Your PTSD?

Many people are often reluctant to let their bosses know what they are experiencing as regards their mental health. Some individuals feel it is not necessary for personal reasons, while others feel it may be a threat to their job if they disclose this information.

But the truth is that the symptoms of PTSD affect your job either way and can lead to you losing it. What's more, if nobody knows what you are dealing with, then there will be no way for you to get the support you need from your employer.

It is imperative that you tell your boss what you are going through. This will help you develop an open and honest work environment. It is also a fantastic way to get relief. Most times, opening up makes you feel like you are no longer alone. Your boss may provide outlets to help make your condition more manageable, and with time things will start to improve.

How Can Your Boss Help?

Your boss or employer can help establish an environment of support, awareness, and tolerance. All of these will help ensure you can perform at an optimum level even with your condition.

The following are some of the other ways your boss can help with your condition:

- Offering you additional time to finish up tasks that are not urgent

- Providing you the opportunity to adjust your schedule as you see feet so you can fit in your treatment appointments

- Adding more light to the workplace to enable you to concentrate better

- Allowing you to rearrange items around the office that can trigger your PTSD symptoms

- Permitting you to arrange your office furniture in a way that suits you and makes you comfortable

Chapter 7:

Painting a Brighter Future

The battle does not end after treatment and recovery from PTSD. You will still have to rebuild your life, now that you can see the potential and opportunity lying in front of you.

Many people find it difficult to go beyond this stage and find themselves slipping back into all of the symptoms they tried everything possible to escape from.

To ensure this does not happen to you, it will be important to learn strategies that will help you build the kind of future you desire.

In order to begin, the first thing you will require is a positive mindset.

Why Have a Positive Mindset?

Your mindset can influence your success, growth, and your plan for a better future. What you think about continually becomes your reality. This is because it becomes evident in your behavior and, with time, in your overall life. This makes it extremely crucial that you do all you can to have the right one.

Your mindset is something that can help you achieve success or help you fail. And if your goal is to get the best future after recovery, then it will be essential that you master your mindset.

If that is not convincing enough, consider these other more reasons to be positive:

It Can Help With Self-Esteem

Having a positive growth mindset can help you develop strong and healthy self-esteem. It is a vital tool that has an impact on how we talk to ourselves. If your mindset is negative, you will certainly have more negative self-talk, which can plant negativity in your life. For someone who is recovering from PTSD, this is certainly not where you want to be.

On the other hand, having a positive growth mindset can help ensure you plant positivity and inspiration in your life, both of which are crucial to success.

It Helps you Develop a Winning Viewpoint

When it comes to growth and planning for your future, your perspective is important. The way we choose to associate meaning to circumstances and events can have a huge influence on the way we see life.

Mindset is closely associated with our viewpoint and perspectives. Our core attitudes and beliefs have a natural influence on the way we experience our surroundings and process information. When you have an optimistic mindset, it enhances the possibility of you developing a winning viewpoint and attaining the success you want for your future.

It Helps with Motivation

Your mindset is vital to your level of motivation. With the right mindset that urges you to be focused and grow, you can easily go beyond your comfort zones. When you are motivated, you will have the urge to achieve more. Your mindset offers you this benefit.

It Aids in Dealing with Adversity

When you are chasing a better future, you are most likely going to face some obstacles on the way. To get through these obstacles, it will be vital to learn to deal with all of these challenges by facing them head-on.

Mindset is crucial in getting through these adversities. Adversities can test your resilience and make you give up before achieving your goals. However, the right mindset can help you get back up and keep pushing even in the face of adversities until you achieve your goals.

It Helps You Achieve Goals

Without the right mindset, you may never achieve any goal. To achieve a goal, you need more than just the zeal to achieve success. Your mindset can determine if you will accept defeat or attain the success you need.

Having a positive mindset can ensure you pursue your objectives to the end until you get the results you are after.

How to Develop Your Mindset for Success?

People who achieve the best results have what they want in their sights and do everything possible to achieve it. If their major priority is to build a home, they focus on it and constantly develop their abilities.

Their minds help them develop beliefs and motivations that will help them achieve success. In essence, they have a mindset for success, which is why they tend to achieve much more than others in their field.

If you are serious about working towards a better future after your PTSD recovery, then you will need this mindset too. The good news is that it is possible to build a successful mindset using the right information.

See your Mindset as a Voice

Your mindset controls the way you act and the way you talk. It has an impact on how you talk to yourself. Once you recognize this fact, you are on your way to getting a growth mindset.

If you notice your inner voice is always trying to undermine your efforts by telling you it is impossible, or you can't do it, then you have a fixed mindset. Instead, learn to think big. Get rid of the word impossible from your dictionary because it is a negative word that implies failure.

The reality of the mindset is that you start to become what you think. So, make a list of reasons as to why you can do something. The moment you start to see things as possible, your mind will begin to work towards creating solutions for you instead.

Just by thinking big, you can set off a chain reaction of other thoughts that will help you find your passion and develop the life of your dreams.

Keep A Positive Attitude at All Times

A positive attitude can be instrumental in helping you achieve your goals. It is one of the best ways to develop a success mindset. It can be easy to be frustrated when you deal with setbacks in the process of achieving specific goals.

Having a positive attitude means that you pick the lessons from any setbacks or failures, instead of giving up or being sad about it. This will make it easy to deal with small failures and help you continue heading towards your goals.

Positive thinking helps you draw more people in with your personality. These individuals can even offer you some support on your journey to creating a better future.

Positive thinking also tends to make you a more pleasant person to be around, allowing you to attract support from others who can help you along the way.

Take A Step Even When You Are Afraid

When you want to build your confidence, you will need to get out of your comfort zone. Taking little steps each day out of situations you are comfortable with will give you a better handle on your life and help you achieve goals.

If you are working towards huge goals and working towards the future of your dreams, you will need to get out of your comfort zone. Even though it can be scary at first, the success that comes with it will be worth it.

Establish Goals that Align With Your Priorities

Regardless of the effort you put in, or the amount of success you have acquired, you may not feel fulfilled if you are not living a life based on your priorities.

You need to have a clear definition of what a successful life means to you. Does it mean having the best cars or having a strong savings account? Does it mean building a huge home in the city or being kind to the needy?

It is essential to think about what success means to you, then set goals that are in line with your priority. This will ensure the version of success you are working towards attaining is one that makes you feel fulfilled.

Establish a Growth Mindset

Successful individuals know the importance of growth and believe in it. They believe that as they gain experience, their skills will improve. They believe they will find all they need to get the outcome they desire.

If we are certain that we will get past any obstacles that come our way, we learn from them and continue to try until we find something that works. Everything that comes with the growth mindset is sure to help you attain success.

Don't Compete with Anyone

It is not a bad idea to copy the actions and strategies of people who have attained what you are trying to. By doing this, we can learn from some of the mistakes they made and avoid them. In essence, we are following a path that has already been proven to work, which means you will get to your destination quickly.

However, learning from them is one thing, but trying to compete with them in our minds can never turn outright. If you do this, you may begin to doubt your capacity, and this may lead to you giving up earlier than you should have.

Instead, it is best to compete with yourself alone. This will ensure you are focused on just you and not do what any other person is doing. You are focused on achieving your goals and being in a better position than you were before.

Remember that developing a mindset for success does not happen overnight. However, this does not mean that it is impossible. Continue to use the strategies above to work on your mindset, and you will soon observe the amazing changes in your life.

Finding Your Life Goals

It is one thing to create goals and achieve them, but it is another to create goals that you are genuinely passionate about. Many people hurriedly set goals that don't align with their lives and end up being frustrated or demotivated along the line.

In essence, you have to find your life goals. However, how exactly does one find these kinds of goals? This is where many people tend to have a problem as they don't know how to even find their life goals in the first instance.

List Out what is Crucial to You

The first step when it comes to finding your life goal is to list out the most essential things to you. Regardless of how strange they may seem, list them out. It does not matter what it is, as all you need to do is list out the goals based on their priority.

For instance, here is my sample list: My family, my car, my dogs, and my sound system.

This is just to give you a perspective of where your life is presently.

Determine why Every Item on Your List is Crucial

Why are the items on your list vital to you? Using mine as an example;

- My family because they mean the world to me. They provide me with warmth, support, and companionship, all of which keep me sane and happy

- My car because it is beautiful and makes me look presentable anytime I arrive at a meeting venue

- My dogs because they are absolutely remarkable. They protect my family and I, are loyal to a fault, and provide me with companionship

- My sound system because I love music. It allows me to listen to songs that soothe my spirit

Point Out Your Values Using the Answers

Search for what your answers are centered on. When you read through the list, what resonates with you that you see a few times? Are there items on the list that are similar to each other? In my list, the following themes are common: support, companionship, and family.

The themes we point out echo our values and those things that are crucial to us in our lives. It is from this point you should begin setting your goals.

Set Goals Using Your Values

Any goal you find inspiring will most likely be centered on what is vital to you and your values. If you search deeply, there is a significant chance that you are already working towards achieving a few of them.

Nonetheless, below are a few things you should consider when setting your goals:

- **Don't Go all out to Set Huge Goals**. For instance, a goal of becoming a billionaire in the next two months may sound fun and ambitious, but aiming that high sets yourself up for disappointment. You may never achieve that, and this may leave you frustrated in the long run

- **Set Goals in Smaller Chunks**. Now that you're thinking more practically and scaling down from $1,000,000,000, you might still be feeling daunted by the idea of saving $20,000 this year. However, a goal of saving $4,000 in the next three months sounds like something achievable

- **Ensure your Goals are Positive**. Your goals should involve you working towards achieving something you desire, not as a way for you to escape from something undesirable. For instance, "I want to build a huge home" is a goal that sounds positive

- **Understand that your goals may change as you work towards them.** This tends to happen because, as we work, we learn new things. This new knowledge helps us mold our already set goals into more appealing ones. In the end, you may move to a goal even better than what you set beforehand

In essence, when you develop your life goals from your values, they make you feel more fulfilled and motivated. You are urged to work towards these goals and achieve the results you desire.

The Five Golden Rules For Successful Goal Setting

If you want to set goals that work, you will have to follow some rules. If there are no rules guiding your goals, you may find yourself with the wrong set of goals that don't motivate or inspire you. If this happens, you will soon abandon these goals after having wasted time and effort you could have invested into something else.

In order to make certain that this does not happen to you, these rules can be of help.

Set Goals That Inspire You

If you set a goal, it has to be one that motivates you. It means that they have to be crucial to you, as we discussed above, and there is something that you stand to benefit from achieving these goals.

If you don't have that much interest in the results, or they don't align to the values you have, it will be very difficult for you to be motivated and put in the needed effort to see these goals through. Motivation is extremely crucial when it comes to achieving goals.

Set goals that motivate you and are a priority in your life. If you are not focused, you may end up with numerous goals, and it will be impossible to devote the time needed to achieve any of them. If you want to achieve goals, it is vital for you to be committed. So, if you want to increase your possibility of success, you will require the push that comes from motivation.

If you don't have this, you may not be willing to put in the effort needed to achieve the goals, and in the end, you will be demotivated and frustrated. You may also start to see yourself as a failure, and this may be detrimental to other aspects of your life.

Set SMART Goals

If you want your goals to have the kind of pull they need, it is vital for them to be SMART. This is an acronym that stands for:

- Specific.

- Measurable.

- Attainable.

- Relevant.

- Time-Bound

All of your goals should have the features above if you are serious about results. Let us take a deeper look into how you can incorporate each below.

Set Specific Goals

Your goals have to be properly defined. It should show you a clear path of what you need to achieve. Make it easy for yourself by ensuring it is properly defined and specific.

Set Measurable Goals

If you are unable to measure your results, how can you tell if you are making any headway? If you set a goal, which is simply written as "To save money," how will you determine if you are already successful. Does $10 in your account count as success?

Instead, a measurable goal should be to save $4,000. This way, you know the level of progress you are making and know when you have hit the mark to begin celebrations.

Set Attainable Goals

Be certain that your goals can be achieved. If you set a goal that is impossible to achieve even with your best efforts, it will only harm you and your goals. What's more, it can tell on your confidence and leave you feeling demoralized.

Still, this does not mean you should set extremely easy goals. Accomplishing these kinds of goals may not offer you the feeling you want. There is no fun in achieving something you did not have to work towards achieving.

In essence, you need to set realistic goals that will still pose a challenge. This way, when you do achieve them, you will feel fulfilled and satisfied.

Set Relevant Goals

Your goals should align with where you are headed in life and your values like we discussed earlier. When you do this, you will develop the focus you require to do the work involved. Setting goals that are irrelevant to you will only result in you wasting your effort and time.

Set Time-Bound Goals

There must be a deadline attached to your goals. This will help you know when it is time to celebrate. When there is a deadline in place, you will work towards achieving goals faster.

Write Down your Goals

Writing down your goal makes it feel real. What's more, it will ensure you do not forget about the goal since you can always go back to read this goal. When writing the goals, try to use "will" as opposed to "might."

For instance, write, "I will save $4,000 this year" instead of "I might save $4,000 this year." The first goal seems powerful, and you can envision yourself saving the $4,000. On the other hand, the second does not show any passion and gives you an escape route.

Remember to write your goal statement in a positive manner. You may also want to use a To-Do list and include all of your goals. Then, place it somewhere in your home where you will see this list each day. This could be on your refrigerator, desk, or walls. This way, it will serve as a constant reminder of what you need to do.

Develop an Action Plan

Many people tend to miss this process when setting goals. They tend to pay so much attention to the results that they don't remember to plan all the steps they will require as they go on.

It is ideal to write a detailed action plan that covers all the steps you will need to take to accomplish your goal. When you complete a step you can cross it out, which will show you how close you are getting to your main objective.

This is particularly crucial if you have a huge and tedious goal you wish to achieve.

See it Through

Goal setting is a continuous activity, and not something you do for a while and stop. This is the problem many individuals have, which is why many new year resolutions never get past the first month.

If you want to achieve your goal, you will need to see it as something ongoing. To do this, create reminders to keep you in line and review your goals frequently. This will help you see the progress you have made so far and the areas you can adjust.

Listing out the things you plan to achieve is one thing, but actually seeing it through to the end is another process entirely. If you don't explicitly define your goals and understand your reasons for setting them, you are most likely not going to succeed.

However, following these rules above can ensure you get the best results when it comes to your goals.

Routine and the Role it Plays

When trying to make room for recovery, it may be important to make adjustments to your regular life. This is where having a routine can be helpful. With a routine, you can feel more in control of every aspect of your life and make allocations for other important things.

Routines can help you deal with change and help keep your mind healthy and positive. What's more, they can make it easier to achieve the goals you have set for yourself. All of these benefits make routines extremely crucial for people who are trying to build their lives back once more.

A routine can add structure in your life and help reduce stress. It has to do with being self-disciplined so you can become the person you desire to be.

That being said, let us take a look at a few ways to develop a routine in your life.

How to Build a Routine

Decide on the Type of Routine

The first thing you need to do is determine the kind of routine you want to develop in your life. Is it morning, afternoon, etc.? Many people prefer a morning routine because mornings can seem like the most difficult.

Look for Your Motive

Think about why beginning a routine is vital to you. What is your reason for creating a routine? Do you want to be more focused on your goals? Or do you want to stop sleeping in excess?

Be specific about your reason for starting a routing because it will ensure you are more motivated and put in the needed effort.

Alter Your Present Routine

Evaluate your present routine and see if there are any changes you could make. Maybe you want to stop spending so much or want to eat out less. You need to consider the things you need to do each day irrespective of if you like doing them or not. For instance, taking the dog for a walk or cleaning your home even when you don't want to.

Consider the things you will love to include in your present routine. Would you like to write every evening before bed? Or would you want to read a book?

List out some realistic things you will love to include in your routine, then pick out three or more of the most important ones.

Arrange Them

List out what your perfect routine looks like with the things you want to do and those things you need to do. Then, arrange them in a reasonable manner. Consider the amount of time you would like to invest in each habit or activity. However, you need to also consider the amount of time you have available to make this work.

If your goal is to cut down your expenses by 10%, and you have another goal that will increase your expenses by 40%, then how will you make this possible?

Make certain that you don't commit yourself to more than you can handle. This will only make it difficult to complete your routine.

Make it Work

Since you have set up a plan, the next step is to begin to implement it. Try to write down your routine and paste it in locations you can easily spot so you won't forget your goal.

Incorporate a new routine and see how it feels. Don't forget that it is possible to alter your routine if you are not pleased with how it feels. Your routines don't have to be fixed. Try to make them flexible enough so you can change them when you want.

Now that you know how to develop a routine, let us look at a few things you can incorporate into various times of the day.

Developing a Healthy Morning Routine

In most cases, the time you wake up each day marks the start of your day. For this reason, whatever you choose to do as soon as you wake up is very important. This is because it can make your day amazing or terrible.

That is why it is crucial to incorporate healthy habits into your mornings. Even if your mornings have never been amazing since you could remember, there are some ways to make certain that you begin your morning right.

Getting quality sleep is a great way to do so. You will also need to incorporate the habit of waking up as soon as your alarm rings. If you don't, you are subconsciously implying that you are not ready for the day and want to push it for later.

On the other hand, if you wake up with passion and excitement about how you can benefit from the new day, then it will most likely come your way.

You can supplement your morning routine with activities like:

- **Eat Breakfast.** Eat a balanced breakfast to provide your body with energy. Add proteins like salmon, or eggs, alongside healthy grains like oatmeal. It is crucial to consume breakfast each day to enjoy peak health.

- **Drink a glass of water.** Drinking water offers benefits to both your mind and body. It rehydrates you and fuels your brain so you can enjoy a productive day. It can also help balance your appetite by ensuring you are not confusing hunger with dehydration.

- **Stretch.** When you wake up, it is normal to feel stiff and groggy. To deal with this, stretch a little so you can become energized enough to begin a productive day.

Other things you can do include:

- Mediate for some minutes.

- Write down some things you are thankful for.

- Visualize a productive day.

- Do some Exercise.

- Write or go through your to-do list for the day.

If you incorporate all of these into your life, the difference in your focus, mood, health, and relationships will be amazing.

Daily Routines

One of the best ways you can develop your life each day is to take frequent breaks while engaging in any task.

This is the case regardless of if you are working at home, traveling, running an organization, or working in the office. If you are working, your mind is certainly going to be occupied, which will mean you will require time to free up your mind once in a while.

Regular breaks can help enhance your concentration and focus. They also result in improved mental health and mood. Your goal should be to recharge for about 40 minutes to one hour.

However, this does not mean you should get carried away and forget about the task at hand. Your goal should be to take breaks frequently to help your mind function the way it should.

It is very important to stay active. There are numerous little habits that you can develop to ensure this is possible even if you sit in the office all day.

First, you can take a walk each day, or stretch on your seat for a few minutes after one to two hours. Also, you can take the stairs as often as you can instead of the elevator or use the bike to work if possible.

Developing Healthy Evening Routines

Similar to a morning routine, there are great evening routines you can incorporate in your life too.

Having a great evening routine can help you de-stress and ensure all of the good work you have completed does not go to waste.

The following are a few evening routines you can try out:

Plan for Tomorrow

By now, you probably know the importance of a good plan. It is common knowledge which not everybody implements.

Creating a plan for the next day will help you wake up knowing what exactly you need to do and why. If you start your day without having a plan, your day may most likely go without direction.

Set aside no less than five to 10 minutes each night to list out the things you want to achieve the following day. This simple but effective routine can ensure you end the day fulfilled and start the next day with direction.

Spend Time with Family

Family is crucial, and regardless of how busy you are, you need to make conscious efforts to spend time with them.

One of the best moments to do this is in the evening. Bonding with your family will only offer you benefits in the long run.

You are probably trying to get them and yourself a better future, which is probably why you are making so much effort in the first place. So, do all you can to ensure you don't forget.

You can always clear up your work some other time. However, the time you waste not spending with your loved ones something that you can never clear up.

Do Something Your Enjoy

Many people tend to get so engrossed with work that they forget to do things they enjoy. All of their efforts and time goes into making their goals a reality.

However, life is not just about work. You need to enjoy what you worked for as well. What's more, doing something you enjoy can help you feel refreshed and accomplished.

Allocate a few minutes of your evening to do something you enjoy. Regardless of if it is calling someone you love, playing a game or musical instrument, or spending time with your family.

Let yourself reap the efforts from all the hard work you have been doing. Try to do something you love each night.

Other habits you can add to your evening routine include:

- Avoiding excess food before bed

- Taking a bath

- Turning off all your electronic gadgets before bed

- Doing a review of how you spent your day

There are numerous healthy routines you can begin to incorporate into your life today. Nonetheless, the options above will provide you with the results you want if done right.

Conclusion

PTSD is real and highly inconveniencing for anyone who experiences it. However, it is possible to get past it using all of the information we have covered in this book.

Remember that it requires commitment to get over this issue. There are numerous treatment options you can pick from like those we covered in chapter two. As a recap, they are:

- Cognitive Processing Therapy (CPT)

- Prolonged Exposure Therapy

- Eye Movement Desensitization and Reprocessing (EMDR)

- Stress Inoculation Training (SIT)

- Medications

If these treatments are not an option for you, there are also self-care strategies you can implement to help you deal with your condition. Some common self-care you can try out are:

- Mindful Breathing

- Workout

- Eat Healthy

- Pamper Yourself

- Say No

- Help Others

- Move More

There are many self-care strategies to choose from, and all you need to do is choose an option that works for you.

Also, when it involves PTSD, writing down your thoughts on a journal can give you the seamless recovery you need. Doing this can help you clear your head and vent so you can feel better. Journaling can also help you deal with anxiety and stress, both of which are symptoms of PTSD. If you don't know how to go about writing a journal, we covered all you need to know in chapter three.

Self-awareness, which means having a conscious feeling of your character and person, is also another way to get peace within yourself. It helps you clear up all of the confusing emotions that tend to come with PTSD. If you want to improve your overall life, don't forget that self-awareness is key.

To be self-aware, you can practice mindfulness, keep a journal, practice the art of listening, and so on. Anytime you feel you are navigating through life without being aware, you can head back to read all of the information stated in chapter four. This will help bring you back into a state of awareness, and ensure that PTSD does not take control of your life.

Another thing to note is that PTSD may also cause one to think negative thoughts. Since negative thoughts can lead to other damaging feelings like low self-esteem, and feelings of worthlessness, it will be extremely crucial that you learn to phase out these thoughts and replace them with positive ones.

To go about this, you can challenge and question these thoughts, or take advantage of positive self-supportive statements. As a reminder, some helpful self-talk statements are:

- I am relevant.

- I am not worthless.

- I have the power to control my thoughts.

PTSD affects your intimate and family relationships. It even affects your relationship with your friends and coworkers. But there are a lot of things you can do to make certain you don't lose the relationships that are important to you. Some top options are:

- Getting treatment.

- Using your prescribed medication.

- Finding out more about your condition.

- Sharing your feelings with someone.

Lastly, don't forget that even with how destructive PTSD may seem, it is possible to get treatment and get control of your life. Never forget this fact, as this will help you stay motivated throughout the treatment process. You deserve a good life, and you have the power to get it.

I am not promising that you won't face any problems as you go on. However, I have laid out all of the information in a manner anybody can understand with ease, and all you have to do is read through, understand, and incorporate each one in your life.

I hope you get the future you desire after reading this book. I see you conquering your PTSD and taking full charge of your life.

Thank you for giving me the chance to help you through this turbulent time. If you enjoyed this book or found it helpful to you, please give it a positive review.

References

2011-2020, (c) C. skillsyouneed.com. (n.d.). The Importance of Mindset. Retrieved from https://www.skillsyouneed.com/ps/mindsets.html

Action 16. (n.d.). Retrieved from https://www.actionforhappiness.org/take-action/set-your-goals-and-make-them-happen

Beard, C., Beard, C., BeardHi, C., Mia, Beard, C., Beard, C., ... Amanda. (2019, December 27). How To Create Intentional Routines In Your Life. Retrieved from https://theblissfulmind.com/how-to-create-daily-routine/

Bressert, S. (2018, December 26). How Does PTSD Affect Relationships? Retrieved from https://psychcentral.com/lib/ptsd-and-relationships/

Clear, J. (2013, February 19). 7 Simple Steps to Build a Successful Mindset. Retrieved from https://www.lifehack.org/articles/communication/straightforward-formula-for-living-your-success.html

DSM-5 Criteria for PTSD. (2019, April 10). Retrieved from https://www.brainline.org/article/dsm-5-criteria-ptsd

Ellis, M. E. (2019, July 10). Can You Work With PTSD? Understanding How PTSD Affects Daily Function. Retrieved from https://www.bridgestorecovery.com/blog/can-you-work-with-ptsd-understanding-how-ptsd-affects-daily-function/

Fabello, M. A. (2014, July 29). 5 Steps Toward Effectively Communicating Your Feelings. Retrieved from https://everydayfeminism.com/2014/02/effectively-communicating-feelings/

Hammond, C. (2017, October 18). Difference between PTSD reactions and Borderline Personality Disorder. Retrieved from https://pro.psychcentral.com/exhausted-woman/2017/10/difference-between-ptsd-reactions-and-borderline-personality-disorder/

Hardy, B. (2019, July 19). Why Keeping a Daily Journal Could Change Your Life. Retrieved from https://medium.com/better-humans/why-keeping-a-daily-journal-could-change-your-life-9a4c11f1a475

Jacobson, T., Jacobson, T., & Engku. (2017, September 20). Increasing Self-Awareness Of Triggers in Addiction Recovery. Retrieved from https://addictionblog.org/recovery/increasing-self-awareness-of-triggers-in-addiction-recovery/

Lee, N. (2019, April 11). 5 Proven Ways to Set Goals and Achieve Them. Retrieved from https://medium.com/swlh/5-proven-ways-to-set-goals-and-achieve-them-cf19016b3af1

Lorenzo, C. de. (2018, August 20). 7 Self-Care Strategies You Can Use To Manage Trauma Triggers, According To Experts. Retrieved from https://www.bustle.com/p/7-self-care-strategies-to-help-manage-trauma-according-to-experts-10087377

Maria Cohut, P. D. (n.d.). PTSD: Five effective coping strategies. Retrieved from https://www.medicalnewstoday.com/articles/319824#1.-Mindfulness-meditation

Maria Cohut, P. D. (n.d.). PTSD: Five effective coping strategies. Retrieved from https://www.medicalnewstoday.com/articles/319824#1.-Mindfulness-meditation

Martin, S. (2018, January 7). How to Communicate Your Feelings. Retrieved from https://blogs.psychcentral.com/imperfect/2017/01/how-to-communicate-your-feelings/

Post Traumatic Stress Disorder and Addiction. (n.d.). Retrieved from https://dualdiagnosis.org/mental-health-and-addiction/post-traumatic-stress-disorder-and-addiction/

Prywes, M. (2016, March 11). Keeping A Journal Can Make You Mentally Stronger, Science Explains Why. Retrieved from https://www.lifehack.org/374972/science-explains-why-keeping-a-journal-can-make-you-mentally-stronger

PTSD Self-Help. (2020, January 27). Retrieved from https://www.therecoveryvillage.com/mental-health/ptsd/related/ptsd-self-help-tips/#gref

Self-Care Checklist for Dealing With PTSD Trauma Triggers. (2020, March 23). Retrieved from https://themighty.com/2017/12/how-to-deal-with-post-traumatic-stress-disorder-trauma-triggers-self-care/

Smith, J. A., Smith, J. A., Smith, J. A., Smith, J. A., UC Berkeley, Ggsc, … Ggsc. (n.d.). How to Find Your Purpose in Life. Retrieved from https://greatergood.berkeley.edu/article/item/how_to_find_your_purpose_in_life

Writers, S. (2020, March 20). PTSD in College: Knowing the Signs and Finding Support. Retrieved from https://www.affordablecollegesonline.org/college-resource-center/college-student-ptsd/

Made in the USA
Coppell, TX
16 January 2021

48290914R00092